Milady's Standard Workbook
for Professional Estheticians

Milady's Standard Workbook for Professional Estheticians

To be used with

MILADY'S STANDARD TEXTBOOK FOR PROFESSIONAL ESTHETICIANS

Edited by Jane Morehouse

Milady Publishing
(a division of Delmar Publishers)
3 Columbia Circle, P.O. Box 12519
Albany, New York 12212-2519

NOTICE TO THE READER

COPYRIGHT © 1982, 1992, 1999
Milady is an imprint of Delmar, a division of Thomson Learning. The Thomson Learning logo is a registered trademark used herein under license.

Printed in the United States of America
4 5 6 7 8 9 10 XXX 04 03 02 01 00

For more information, contact Milady, 3 Columbia Circle, PO Box 15015, Albany, NY 12212-0515; or find us on the World Wide Web at http://www.Milady.com

Library of Congress Number: 98-20108

ISBN: 1-56253-360-6

CONTENTS

How to Use this Workbook

This workbook has been especially designed to meet the needs, interests, and abilities of students receiving training for a career in esthetics, the art of skin care. It has been organized to be used in conjunction with *Milady's Standard Textbook for Professional Estheticians.*

The material presented here has been prepared in accordance with the accepted methods of Vocational Training that are approved by State Licensing Organizations. All materials have been compiled with the assistance of leading educators and teachers in the field of esthetics and cosmetology.

1. **Assignment of the Lesson**

   Pages to be read and studied are listed at the top of the page.

2. **Learning the Lesson**

   The student writes the answers in pencil in the workbook, consulting the test and glossary/index located in the back of *Milady's Standard Textbook for Professional Estheticians.*

3. **Correction of the Lesson**

   Answers may be corrected and rated during class discussions.

4. **Review of the Lesson**

   Various tests emphasize the essential facts and measure the student's progress.

INTRODUCTION

Date _____

Rating _____

Text Pages xxvi–xxxvi

TOPIC 1—CAREER OPPORTUNITIES

1. Personal care services are offered by full-service salons. Name six personal care services other than haircare and styling that are given in full-service salons.

   a. _____

   b. _____

   c. _____

   d. _____

   e. _____

   f. _____

2. Estheticians have many opportunities in the cosmetic industry.

   a. Name four career opportunities that may be open for estheticians in the cosmetic industry.

      1. _____

      2. _____

      3. _____

      4. _____

   b. Name four opportunities for estheticians in communications.

      1. _____

      2. _____

      3. _____

      4. _____

   c. Name four opportunities for estheticians in the education field.

      1. _____

      2. _____

      3. _____

      4. _____

d. Name four opportunities for estheticians, outside cosmetology schools, that are related to cosmetology.

1. _____

2. _____

3. _____

4. _____

e. Name four opportunities for estheticians in salons.

1. _____

2. _____

3. _____

4. _____

f. Name three opportunities for estheticians in specialized careers outside the salon.

1. _____

2. _____

3. _____

3. What is the meaning of the word "esthetics"?

_____

Word Review

beauty therapist	esthetician	merchandising
cosmetic buyer	guest artist	plastic surgeon
cosmetician	lecturer	practitioner
dermatologist	makeup artist	restorative art

Rapid Review Test

Date_____

Rating_____

Place the correct word in spaces provided in the sentences below.

dermatologist	plastic surgeon	restorative art
esthetician	practitioner	salesperson
lecturer	representatives	teacher

1. An operation done on the face to correct or beautify its contours is done by a

_____ .

2. The practice of restoring the features of the deceased is called _____ .

3. An _____ specializes in the health and care of the skin.

4. A _____ is a person who speaks on a particular subject before a group.

5. A person who practices a particular art or profession is called a _____ .

6. A good _____ is needed if you expect to learn.

7. Manufacturers of cosmetics often hire _____ to call on salons or stores where cosmetics are sold.

8. An esthetician should also be a competent _____ .

9. A _____ is a physician who specializes in treating the skin.

Your Professional Image

Date _____

Rating _____

Text Pages 1–4

TOPIC 1—HYGIENE

1. The laws of hygiene are the laws of healthful living.

    a. Name two branches of hygiene.

    1. _____

    2. _____

    b. What is the main concern of public hygiene?_____

2. Personal hygiene and body care are important to everyone.

    a. Name six tasks to perform daily to maintain your own personal hygiene and health.

    1. _____

    2. _____

    3. _____

    4. _____

    5. _____

    6. _____

3. Attitudes and emotions influence personality and health. Name three ways you can maintain a healthy attitude.

    a. _____

    b. _____

    c. _____

Word Review

exercise   nutrition   personal hygiene

fatigue   oral hygiene   public hygiene

hygiene

Date_____

Rating_____

Text Pages 4–7

TOPIC 2—POSTURE AND VISUAL POISE

1. Name three benefits of good posture.

   a. _____

   b. _____

   c. _____

2. "Posture," in the broadest sense, describes the carriage of the body when standing, walking, sitting, or stooping.

   a. When standing, over which part of the feet should the weight be balanced?

   _____

   b. When standing or walking, what should you remember to avoid doing with the knees?

   _____

3. Standing properly helps to prevent fatigue. Why is the basic stance preferred to placing the feet side by side?

   _____

4. Correct sitting posture is important to the esthetician. What are the four points of posture the esthetician should remember when sitting to perform a service such as giving a facial?

   a. _____

   b. _____

   c. _____

   d. _____

Word Review

balance   body alignment   poise   visual poise

basic stance   fatigue   visual impression

Rapid Review Test

Date_____

Rating_____

Place the correct word in spaces provided in the sentences below.

| alignment | instep | balls | flexed |

1. When standing, walking, sitting, or stooping, the body should be in proper

   _____ .

2. To avoid throwing the body out of alignment, the knees should be slightly

   _____ .

3. In basic stance, the heel that is forward is placed to the _____ of the foot that is back.

4. When walking or standing, weight should be primarily on the _____ of the feet.

Date _____

Rating _____

Text Pages 7–8

TOPIC 3—HAND, NAIL, AND FOOT CARE

1. An esthetician is expected to have supple, well groomed hands.

   a. Why should the esthetician avoid having nails that are too long and pointed?

   _____

   b. If the esthetician's hands and nails are obviously uncared for, what kind of message will this telegraph to the client?

   _____

2. Give four suggestions for keeping the hands and nails presentable.

   a. _____

   b. _____

   c. _____

   d. _____

3. Bitten nails and cuticles are unsightly. If you have the nail-biting habit, what should you do?

   _____

4. Name four benefits of well fitted shoes.

   a. _____

b. _____

c. _____

d. _____

Word Review

arches   corn   ingrown

bunion   cuticle   malformed

Date_____

Rating_____

Text Pages 8–11

TOPIC 4—PERSONALITY AND HUMAN RELATIONS

1. The professional esthetician should project a winsome personality. Which of the following do you consider to be qualities of a pleasing personality? *Place a checkmark beside your answers.*

   ☐ Healthy attitude toward life   ☐ Politeness

   ☐ Pleasant voice   ☐ Sense of humor

   ☐ Emotional stability   ☐ Graciousness of manner

   ☐ Rudeness   ☐ Bad temper

2. Your speaking voice reflects your personality.

   a. What are the desirable qualities of a pleasant speaking voice? *Place a checkmark beside your answers.*

   ☐ Use correct English.   ☐ Speak with expressiveness.

   ☐ Keep the voice well modulated   ☐ Speak with intelligence.

      (not too soft or too loud).   ☐ Speak with clarity.

   b. Which topics are suitable for conversation with clients? *Place a checkmark beside your answers.*

   ☐ Client's personal interests   ☐ Literature, art, or music

   ☐ Your personal life   ☐ Education and travel

   ☐ Client's activities   ☐ Civic affairs

   ☐ Latest gossip   ☐ Travel or vacations

   c. Clients may be annoyed or offended by the esthetician who does the following. *Place a checkmark beside your answers.*

   ☐ Shows disrespect for clients   ☐ Complains about co-workers

   ☐ Finds fault with others   ☐ Repeats confidential information

   ☐ Constantly complains   ☐ Expresses religious prejudice

☐ Makes sarcastic remarks   ☐ Brags about his or her accomplishments

☐ Discusses personal affairs   ☐ Discusses personal health

3. Professional projection helps you make a good impression. Which of the following points of human relations do you consider professional? *Place a checkmark beside your answers.*

☐ Tact and diplomacy   ☐ Being patient and courteous

☐ Being cheerful and enthusiastic ☐ Being concerned about your clients' needs

☐ Being honest, dependable, and loyal ☐ Having a poor sense of humor

☐ Being punctual   ☐ Finding fault and arguing

Word Review

argumentative	emotional stability	monopolize
attitude	facial grimaces	personality traits
characteristics	human relations	profanity
diplomacy	impatience	slang

Date_____

Rating_____

Text Pages 11-12

TOPIC 5—PROFESSIONAL ETHICS

1. Success in the field of esthetics is based on the observation of professional ethics.

   a. What is meant by "ethics"?

   _____

   _____

   _____

   b. What two benefits result from ethical conduct?

   1. _____

   2. _____

   c. List three practices that are considered poor ethical conduct on the job.

   1. _____

   2. _____

   3. _____

2. Can you tell the difference between good and poor ethics on the job? Check each statement as being either good or poor ethics.

		Good Ethics	Poor Ethics
a.	Sincere belief in ethical conduct	☐	☐
b.	Showing favoritism to some clients	☐	☐
c.	Upholding a good reputation	☐	☐
d.	Making promises to clients that you cannot keep	☐	☐
e.	Giving the best possible service	☐	☐
f.	Being loyal to your employer	☐	☐
g.	Showing the client every consideration and courtesy	☐	☐
h.	Being honest in business, whether giving services or making sales	☐	☐
i.	Making your time count	☐	☐
j.	Maintaining a pleasant manner	☐	☐

3. State in your own words why the professional esthetician should learn the laws, rules, and regulations that govern the practice of esthetics and cosmetology services.

_____

_____

_____

_____

Word Review

attitudes	ethics	questionable
compliance	honesty	reputation
confidence	loyalty	respect
cooperation	mannerisms	standards
courtesy	principles	tact
discourtesy	professional	tolerance

CHAPTER 2

A History of Skin Care and the Use of Cosmetics

Date _____

Rating _____

Text Pages 14–23

TOPIC 1—A BRIEF HISTORY OF SKIN CARE AND THE USE OF COSMETICS

1. People have always been concerned with personal grooming.
   a. To what other sciences was the practice of cosmetology once related?

   _____

   b. How do we know that people of ancient times used cosmetics?

   _____

   c. What was the main cosmetic the Egyptians used to line eyes?

   _____

   d. From which country did the Hebrews bring cosmetics and fragrances back to Judea?

   _____

   e. From what language did we gain the word "cosmetics"?

   _____

   f. The Roman custom of men shaving facial hair was a forerunner of what present-day practice?

   _____

   g. What grooming practices did Asians and Africans have in common?

   _____

2. Concepts of grooming and dress have changed during different ages.
   a. The period in history between classical antiquity and the Renaissance is known as

   _____

b. How did the first motion pictures influence dress and grooming?

_____

c. During the 1970s, there was interest in makeup and hair, but there was also renewed interest in

_____

Word Review

Africans	Elizabethan	public baths
Asians	fragrances	Renaissance
contouring	industrialization	vermillion
cosmetics	kohl	Victorian
cosmetology	Middle Ages	World War II

CHAPTER 3

Bacteriology

Date _____

Rating _____

Text Pages 24–28

TOPIC 1—CLASSIFICATION OF BACTERIA

1. Advances in bacteriology have led to better methods of preventing and controlling contagious diseases in the salon.

   a. What is bacteriology?

   _____

   b. Why should the esthetician study bacteriology?

   _____

   _____

2. Contagious diseases may be spread directly from one person to another, or indirectly by contact with infected objects.

   a. What are bacteria?

   _____

   b. Where are bacteria most numerous?

   _____

   c. Which instrument is used to study bacteria?

   _____

3. Some bacteria cause disease, while most are beneficial.

   a. What name is given to beneficial bacteria? _____

   b. Which bacteria live on dead matter? _____

   c. What name is given to harmful bacteria? _____

d. Give three names for disease-producing bacteria.

1. _____

2. _____

3. _____

e. Which bacteria require living matter for their growth?

_____

4. Bacteria are identified under the microscope by means of their distinctive form or shape.

a. What are the shapes of the following bacteria?

1. Cocci _____

2. Spirilla _____

3. Bacilli_____

4. Staphylococci _____

b. Which bacteria are associated with each of the following?

1. Boils _____

2. Syphilis _____

3. Strep throat _____

4. Tetanus _____

5. Like other living organisms, bacteria must have favorable conditions for their growth and reproduction.

a. Which conditions are favorable for the growth and reproduction of pathogenic bacteria?

_____

b. What kind of bacteria make the practice of sterilization and sanitation necessary?

_____

13

6. Illustrated below are various forms of bacteria. *Identify and place the names of the bacteria in the spaces provided.*

1. _____   4. _____

2. _____   5. _____

3. _____   6. _____

Word Review

anthrax	microscope	spirilla
bacilli	mobility	spore
bacteriology	nonpathogenic	staphylococci
cilia	parasite	sterilization
cocci	pathogenic	streptococci
germ	reproduction	tetanus
growth	sanitation	vegetative
microbe	saprophyte	

Rapid Review Test

Date_____

Rating_____

Place the correct word in spaces provided in the sentences below.

cilia	pathogenic	syphilis
contagious	spore	tetanus
nonpathogenic	streptococci	

1. A _____ forming pathogenic bacteria bacillus is associated with influenza.

2. The disease commonly known as "lockjaw" is known in bacteriology as _____ .

3. A serious venereal disease, _____ , is caused by spirilla.

4. Pus-forming organisms that grow in chains are called _____ .

5. The majority of all bacteria are classified as _____ .

6. Wherever any mobility of bacteria is shown, there are hairlike projections known as _____ or flagella.

7. A disease that can be transmitted from one person to another is considered to be a _____ disease.

8. When _____ bacteria enter the body, infection may occur if the body is unable to cope with the bacteria and their harmful toxins.

Rapid Review Test

Date_____

Rating_____

Place the correct word in spaces provided in the sentences below.

beneficial	immunity	reproduce
contact	living	saprophytes
general	microscope	spores
grow	pathogenic	white
harmful	pediculosis	

1. Bacteria become visible when observed under a _____ .

2. Pathogenic bacteria are _____ ; nonpathogenic bacteria are often _____ .

3. Parasites thrive best on _____ matter as food.

4. Bacteria that use dead matter as food are called _____ .

5. Without food, bacteria will not _____ and _____ .

6. In the presence of unfavorable conditions, the anthrax bacilli will form _____ .

7. The type of infection that involves blood circulation, where bacteria are carried to all parts of the body, is called a _____ infection.

8. A contagious or communicable disease is spread from one person to another by _____ .

9. The ability of the body to fight pathogenic bacteria is called _____ .

10. A person infested with lice is known to have _____ .

11. Nonpathogenic bacteria are found in greater abundance than _____ bacteria.

12. The blood cells that help fight invading bacteria are the _____ cells.

Date_____

Rating_____

Text Pages 28–33

TOPIC 2—BACTERIAL INFECTIONS

1. An infection represents an invasion of the body tissues by pathogenic organisms to the point where they can multiply and cause disease.

   a. Name two kinds of infections.

     1. _____

     2. _____

   b. Which infection is most dangerous? _____

   c. Is pus a sign of infection?_____

2. Every contagious disease is caused by a particular kind of germ, stemming from an object or from someone who has that disease.

   a. By which six ways can bacteria enter the body?

     1. _____

     2. _____

     3. _____

     4. _____

     5. _____

     6. _____

   b. How does the body fight infection? _____

   _____

   _____

3. Harmful bacteria rarely produce disease in a healthy body.

   a. Name two body secretions that discourage bacterial growth.

     1. _____

     2. _____

   b. Which two substances in the blood help to overcome harmful bacteria?

     1. _____

     2. _____

4. Immunity is the power of the body to resist infection. There are two types: natural immunity and acquired immunity.

   a. Upon what does natural immunity depend? _____

   _____

   b. How is acquired immunity achieved? _____

   _____

5. A human disease carrier is a person immune to a disease yet harboring germs that can infect other people. Name two diseases that can be transmitted by a carrier.

   a. _____

   b. _____

Word Review

acquired immunity	general infection	natural immunity
antitoxins	hygienic	pathogenic bacteria
contagious	infection	pus
defensive forces	local infection	vaccination

CHAPTER 4

Sterilization, Disinfection, and Safety in the Salon

Date _____

Rating _____

Text Pages 35–42

TOPIC 1—STERILIZATION AND DISINFECTION

1. In the skin care industry, following strict sterilization and disinfection techniques is important to the well-being of clients and estheticians alike.

   a. Name the five widely used methods of sterilization and disinfection.

   1. _____

   2. _____

   3. _____

   4. _____

   5. _____

   b. Dry heat is a method of sterilizing objects in a temperature range of 320° to 338° F. Name five disadvantages of this method.

   1. _____

   2. _____

   3. _____

   4. _____

   5. _____

   c. There are various types of chemical forms that are used for sterilization and disinfection purposes. Name the two forms.

   1. _____

   2. _____

d. Name the two agencies that regulate liquid sterilants/disinfectants.

1. _____

2. _____

2. Match the following definition. Place the correct word in spaces provided in the sentences below.

glutaraldehyde phenate   demand-release chlorine dioxide   hydrogen peroxide

sodium hypochlorite   ethyl or isopropyl alcohol   phenolics

povidone-iodine   quarternary ammonium

a. A liquid sterilant which sterilizes after 6 hours.

_____

b. Not recommended for high-level disinfection of critical objects.

_____

c. Stable and effective disinfectant when used on noncritical surfaces.

_____

d. A household bleach with a broad spectrum of anti-microbial activity.

_____

e. The CDC has deleted the 3 percent solution as ineffective against bacterial spores, myco-baterium tuberculosis, and fungi.

_____

f. Requires 20 minutes for disinfection.

_____

g. Sold as disinfectants they are anti-fungal, but not anti-sporicidal.

_____

h. Does not cause skin irritation when used.

_____

Word Review

anti-sporicidal	ethyl alcohol	microencapsulated chemicals
autoclave	ethylene oxide gas	mycobaterium tuberculosis
bacterial spores	FDA	phenolics
chemiclave	fungi	povidone-iodine
demand-release chlorine dioxide	glutaraldehyde phenate	pressurized gas
disinfection	hydrogen peroxide	quarternary ammonium
EPA	isopropyl alcohol	sterilization
		sodium hypochlorite

Date_____

Rating_____

Text Pages 42–51

TOPIC 2—OSHA

1. It is OSHA's responsibility to see that working conditions meet standards established by the Occupational Safety and Health Act.

   a. When was the Act established? _____

   b. What governing agency enforces the principles of the Act?

   _____

   c. What is the name for the Centers for Disease Control's recommended policy for workers regarding blood and body fluids? _____

2. The general rule of Universal Protection is to protect yourself from the transmission of bloodborne pathogens.

   a. Name a way to protect yourself from exposure.

   _____

   b. How can HBV and HIV and other infectious diseases be spread?

   _____

3. OSHA recommends that "persons at substantial risk of HBV who are demonstrated or judged likely to be susceptible should be vaccinated."

   a. Name four reasons an employer is not required to make the Hepatitis B vaccine available.

   1. _____

   2. _____

   3. _____

   4. _____

   b. List five points that must be documented regarding an exposure to blood incident in an employee's chart, according to OSHA rulings.

   1. _____

   2. _____

   3. _____

   _____

   4. _____

   5. _____

   _____

4. Personal protective equipment must be used if exposure to bloodborne pathogens is a possibility in the workplace.

    a. Name five examples of such protective equipment that may be used in the salon:

      1. _____

      2. _____

      3. _____

      4. _____

      5. _____

    b. What is the procedure to follow after using protective equipment in the salon?

_____

_____

_____

Word Review

antibody	fluid-resistant gowns	mucous membrane
blood and body fluids	gloves	OSHA
bloodborne pathogens	HBV	storage
disposal	HIV	Universal Protection
eye protection	immune	U.S. Dept. of Labor
face shield or mask	laboratory coats	vaccinated

Rapid Review Test

Date_____

Rating_____

Insert the proper term in the space provided.

measure	deterioration	spills
30 days	fumes	ventilation
labeled	BIOHAZARD label	hypoallergenic gloves
appropriate disinfectant	weigh	

1. Those who are allergic to the gloves normally provided in the salon environment should use

_____ .

2. All work surfaces including bowls and trays should be cleaned with an

_____ .

3. Reusable contaminated sharp container such as sterilizing tray requires the use of a

   _____ .

4. All paper/gauze products must be removed off-site within_____ .

5. Purchase chemicals in small quantities and store them in a cool, dry place to avoid _____ from contact with air, light, or heat.

6. _____ and _____chemicals carefully when mixing.

7. Make sure there is adequate _____ when mixing chemicals.

8. Keep all containers properly _____ .

9. Do not breathe _____ from chemicals or solutions.

10. Avoid _____ when mixing chemicals.

Cells, Anatomy, and Physiology

Date _____

Rating _____

Text Pages 52–57

TOPIC 1—THE HUMAN BODY

1. The body begins as one cell and develops into trillions.

   a. What is a cell?

   _____

   b. Describe protoplasm and its components.

   _____

   _____

2. Match the following structures found in a cell to their definitions. *Insert the proper term in the space provided.*

   cell membrane   cytoplasm   centrosome   nucleus

   a. _____ Encloses the protoplasm and holds the cell together.

   b. _____ Dense protoplasm found in the center, which plays an important part in cell reproduction.

   c. _____ Holds organelles and contains food.

   d. _____ Helps maintain the characteristics of the original cell.

3. Metabolism is a complex chemical process in which cells are nourished and supplied with energy. There are two phases.

   a. What is the phase that builds cellular tissues? _____

b. What is the phase that breaks down cellular tissues? _____

4. Name the five classifications of body tissue.

a. _____   d. _____

b. _____   e. _____

c. _____

5. Match the following. *Insert the proper term in the space provided.*

brain   liver   skin

heart   lungs   stomach and intestines

kidneys

a. _____ Controls the nervous system.

b. _____ Circulates the blood.

c. _____ Supply oxygen to the blood.

d. _____ Removes toxic products of digestion.

e. _____ Excrete water and other waste products.

f. _____ Process food.

g. _____ Both a tissue and an organ.

6. Name the nine systems of the body.

a. _____   f. _____

b. _____   g. _____

c. _____   h. _____

d. _____   i. _____

e. _____

Word Review

anabolism   connective tissue   nucleus

catabolism   cytoplasm   organs

cell   epithelial tissue   protoplasm

cell membrane   metabolism   systems

centrosome   mitosis   tissues

Rapid Review Test

Date_____

Rating_____

Place the correct word in spaces provided in the sentences below.

anabolism   endocrine system   skin   catabolism

mitosis   systems   depend   organs

1. The _____ , a membranous tissue, is the body's largest organ.

2. When a cell reaches maturity, it reproduces by _____ .

3. During _____ , cells absorb water, food, and oxygen.

4. Structures consisting of two or more tissues to accomplish a specific function are called

   _____ .

5. The _____ involves the ductless glands.

6. During _____ , cells consume what they have absorbed, to perform specialized functions.

7. All of the body's systems _____ on one another.

8. Groups of organs that cooperate for a common purpose are called _____ .

Date_____

Rating_____

Text Pages 57–59

TOPIC 2—STUDY OF THE SKELETAL SYSTEM

1. The scientific study of the bones is called "osteology." Other than the teeth, bone is the
   hardest part of the body. There are 206 bones in a human skeleton.

   a. Name the four major functions of the bones.

      1. _____

      2. _____

      3. _____

      4. _____

2. The skull is the skeleton of the head.

   a. Into how many parts is the skull divided?_____

b. What are the parts of the skull called? _____

c. How many bones are found in the cranium? _____

How many bones are found in the face? _____

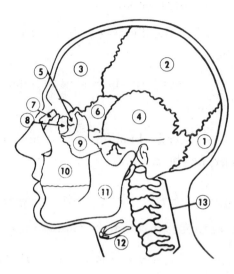

3. Match the following definitions. *Insert the proper term in the space provided.*

cervical vertebrae	occipital	two nasal
ethmoid	sphenoid	two parietal
frontal	two lacrimal	two temporal
hyoid	two maxillae	zygomatic or malar
mandible		

a. _____ Bone that forms the lower back portion of the cranium

b. _____ Bones that form the crown and top of the cranium

c. _____ Bone that forms the forehead

d. _____ Bones that form the sides of the head in the ear region

e. _____ Bones between the eye sockets and that form part of the nasal cavity

f. _____ Bone that joins all the bones of the cranium

g. _____ Bones that form the bridge of the nose

h. _____ Bones located in the front part of the inner wall of the eye socket

i. _____ Bones that form the prominence of the cheeks

j. _____ Bones of the upper jaw

k. _____ Strongest bone of the face—that forms the lower jaw

1. _____ Bone located in the front of the throat

m. _____ Bones that form the top part of the spinal column, located in the neck

4. The esthetician should know the bones that are affected by massage. *Insert the proper term in the space provided.*

   a. Two _____ bones are thin layers of spongy bone situated on either side of the outer walls of the nasal depression.

   b. A single bone that forms part of the dividing wall of the nose is called the _____ bone.

   c. Two _____ bones form the floor and outer wall of the nose, roof of the mouth, and floor of the orbits.

5. The thorax or chest forms a bony cage. In addition to connective cartilage, name the parts that make up the skeleton of the chest.

   a. _____   c. _____

   b. _____   d. _____

6. Match the following definitions. *Insert the proper term in the space provided. (Corresponding numbers appear on the illustration.)*

   carpus   phalanges   scapula   humerus

   radius   ulna   metacarpus

   1. _____ and clavicle (one of each on each side) form the back of the shoulder.

   2. _____ Largest bone of the upper arm.

   3. _____ Large bone on the little finger side of the forearm.

   4. _____ Small bone on the thumb side of the forearm.

   5. _____ or wrist, a flexible joint composed of eight small, irregular bones, held together by ligaments.

   6. _____ or palm consists of five long, slender bones, called metacarpal bones.

   7. _____ Three in each finger and two in the thumb, totaling fourteen bones of the fingers, or digits.

27

Word Review

bones	lacrimal	skeleton
carpus	ligaments	skull
cartilage	mandible	sphenoid
cervical	maxilla	system
clavicle	metacarpus	temporal
cranium	nasal	thorax
crown	occipital	turbinal
digits	palatine	ulna
ethmoid	parietal	vertebrae
frontal	phalanges	vomer
humerus	radius	zygomatic
hyoid	scapula	

Rapid Review Test

Date_____

Rating_____

Place the correct word in spaces provided in the sentences below.

cranium	mineral	shape
humerus	muscles	sphenoid
injury	occipital	temporal
mandible	parietal	ulna
metacarpal		

1. Bone is composed of about two-thirds _____ matter.

2. Bones give strength and _____ to the body.

3. The skull is divided into two parts: the skeleton of the face and the _____ .

4. Bones serve as attachments for _____ .

5. Bones protect body organs from _____ .

6. The lower jawbone is called the _____ .

7. The bones that form the sides and top of the cranium are called the _____ bones.

8. The bones that are located on either side of the skull below the parietal bones are the _____ bones.

9. The bone that forms the back and lower part of the cranium is the _____ bone.

10. The bone that joins all the bones of the cranium is the _____ bone.

11. The largest bone of the upper arm is the _____ .

12. The large bone on the little finger side of the forearm is the _____ .

13. The palm consists of five _____ bones.

Date_____

Rating_____

Text Pages 59–64

TOPIC 3—MUSCULAR SYSTEM (MYOLOGY)

1. The scientific study of muscles, their structure, and their functions is called "myology." The function of the muscular system is to produce the various movements of the body.

   a. About how many muscles are in the body? _____

   b. Muscles compose approximately what percent of body weight? _____

   c. Name three kinds of muscular tissue.

   1. _____

   2. _____

   3. _____

2. When a muscle contracts, one of its attachments usually remains fixed and the other one moves.

   a. What is the name of the fixed muscle attachment? _____

   b. What is the name of the movable muscle attachment? _____

3. Muscular tissue may be stimulated in many ways. Name six methods that can be used to stimulate muscular tissue.

   a. _____   d. _____

   b. _____   e. _____

   c. _____   f. _____

4. The epicranius or occipito frontalis is a broad muscle that covers the top of the skull. It consists of two parts, the occipitalis and the frontalis. Which part lifts the eyebrows?

---

5. The muscles of the eyebrows, nose, and mouth are important because they can produce various kinds of facial expressions. Name the facial muscle that—

a. Surrounds the margin of the eye socket and closes the eyelids, as in blinking.

_____

b. Draws the eyebrow downward and inward, as in frowning. _____

c. Wrinkles the bridge of the nose. _____

d. Produces an expression of distaste. _____

e. Produces a sarcastic expression. _____

f. Contracts and compresses the cheeks, as in blowing. _____

g. Raises the angle of the mouth, as in snarling. _____

h. Wrinkles the chin, as in doubt. _____

i. Puckers the lips, as in kissing or whistling. _____

j. Produces a grinning expression. _____

k. Produces a laughing expression. _____

l. Opens and closes jaws and draws back the lower jaw, as in chewing. _____

6. Muscles attached to the ear are practically functionless. Name the three muscles of the ear.

a. _____   c. _____

b. _____

7. Muscles in the neck and back move the head, neck, and shoulder.

a. Which muscle depresses the lower jaw and lip, as in a sad expression?

_____

b. Which muscle flexes the head, as in nodding?

_____

c. Which muscles rotate the shoulder blades and control the swinging movements of the arm?

_____

d. Which muscles also assist in raising the arm and in swinging movements?

_____

8. Where on the body is each of the following muscles located? *Insert the proper term in the space provided.*

   back   eyebrow   nose
   chest   mouth   scalp
   ear   neck   temple

   a. _____ Orbicularis oris

   b. _____ Epicranius

   c. _____ Corrugator

   d. _____ Procerus

   e. _____ Auricularis superior

   f. _____ Platysma

   g. _____ Temporalis

   h. _____ Pectoralis major

   i. _____ Latissimus dorsi

9. Name three principal muscles of the upper arm and shoulder.

   a. _____   c. _____

   b. _____

10. The muscles of the forearm are responsible for the graceful movements of the hand and wrist. Name the four types of muscles found in the forearm.

    a. _____   c. _____

    b. _____   d. _____

11. Match the following muscles with the following movements. *Insert the proper term in the space provided.*

    extensors   pronators   flexors   supinators

    a. _____ Straighten fingers and hand.

    b. _____ Turn hand outward.

    c. _____ Bend wrist and hand.

    d. _____ Turn hand inward.

Nasal Muscles

12. Identify and insert the names of the muscles shown on the diagram.

1. _____   13. _____

2. _____   14. _____

3. _____   15. _____

4. _____   16. _____

5. _____   17. _____

6. _____   18. _____

7. _____   19. _____

8. _____   20. _____

9. _____   21. _____

10. _____   22. _____

11. _____   23. _____

12. _____   24. _____

Word Review

anterior	extensor	phalanges
aponeurosis	flexors	posterior
biceps	inferior	pronators
cardiac	insertion	proximal
cartilage	involuntary	skeletal
connective	lateral	striated
contractibility	latissimus dorsi	superior
deltoid	ligament	supinators
depressor	nonstriated	tendon
digits	origin	trapezius
distal	pectoralis major	triceps
dorsal	pectoralis minor	voluntary
elasticity		

Rapid Review Test

Date_____

Rating_____

Place the correct word in spaces provided in the sentences below.

50	insertion	oris
500	mastication	risorius
bones	occipitalis	sterno-cleido-mastoid
corrugator	occipito frontalis	top
ear	oculi	will
heart	origin	zygomaticus

1. Muscles comprise about 40% to _____ % of body weight.

2. Skeletal muscles are usually attached to _____ .

3. Aponeurosis is a tendon that connects the frontalis with the _____ .

4. Voluntary muscles are controlled by the _____ .

5. The cardiac muscle is found only in the _____ .

6. The word _____ refers to the more fixed attachment of a muscle.

7. The word _____ refers to the more movable attachment of a muscle.

8. There are about _____ muscles in the body.

9. The epicranius is also known as the _____ .

10. The epicranius covers the _____ of the skull.

11. The masseter is a muscle of _____ .

12. The _____ follows the eyebrow line.

13. The orbicularis _____ surrounds the margin of the eye socket.

14. The orbicularis _____ forms a band around the upper and lower lips.

15. The muscles of the _____ are practically functionless.

16. Laughing and smiling involve the action of the _____ .

17. A grinning facial expression involves the action of the _____ .

18. The muscle that flexes the head as in nodding is the _____ .

Date_____

Rating_____

Text Pages 64–70

TOPIC 4—NERVOUS SYSTEM

1. The nervous system is one of the most important systems of the body.
   a. Define neurology.

   _____

   _____

   b. What is the major function of the nervous system?

   _____

   c. What is the main purpose in studying the nervous system?

   _____

   _____

2. The nervous system may be referred to as the ruler of the body.
   a. Name the principal parts of the nervous system.

   _____

   b. Name the three main divisions of the nervous system.

   1. _____

   2. _____

   3. _____

c. Which functions are controlled by the cerebro-spinal nervous system?

_____

_____

d. What is the function of the peripheral nervous system?

_____

e. Which functions are controlled by the sympathetic nervous system?

_____

3. The nervous system is made up of nerve cells.

　　a. What is another term for "nerve cell"?

　　_____

　　b. What are the two main parts of a nerve cell?

　　_____

　　c. In which two parts of the body are most nerve cells found?

　　　　1. _____

　　　　2. _____

　　d. What parts of the body are influenced by nerve activity?

　　_____

4. Nerves are long, white cords made up of fibers.

　　a. Name two types of nerves.

　　　　1. _____

　　　　2. _____

　　b. What is the common term for—

　　　　1. Afferent nerve? _____

　　　　2. Efferent nerve? _____

　　c. Which nerves send messages from—

　　　　1. Sense organs to the brain? _____

　　　　2. Brain to the muscles? _____

5. The spinal cord is the path through which various sensations are carried to and from the brain.

　　a. Which structure protects the delicate spinal cord? _____

　　b. How many pairs of nerves originate from the spinal cord? _____

6. Proper nutrition and rest help overcome fatigue.

　　a. What are the basic causes of fatigue?

　　_____

35

b. What are four signs of nerve exhaustion?

1. _____   3. _____

2. _____   4. _____

c. How can nerve fatigue be relieved?

_____

7. The nervous system is benefited by the proper use of stimulation. Give one or two examples of ways to stimulate nerves by means of—

a. Chemical_____

b. Massage _____

c. Electric current _____

d. Dry heat _____

e. Moist heat _____

8. Important to the esthetician are the cranial nerves, which control the various movements of the head, face, and neck.

a. How many pairs of cranial nerves originate in the brain? _____

b. Cranial nerves are classified as motor, sensory, and _____ , containing both motor and sensory fibers.

9. Nerve connections between the sense organs and the brain make possible the functions of seeing, hearing, smelling, and tasting. Which function is performed by the following nerves?

a. Olfactory nerve _____   c. Acoustic nerve _____

b. Optic nerve _____   d. Glossopharyngeal nerve _____

10. Certain cranial nerves are affected by facial and scalp treatments.

a. Name three cranial nerves affected by facial and scalp massage.

1. _____

2. _____

3. _____

b. Which nerve originating from the spinal cord is also affected by neck massage?

_____

11. The largest of the cranial nerves is the fifth cranial nerve.

a. List two other names by which the fifth cranial nerve is known.

1. _____

2. _____

b. Which branch of the bifacial nerve supplies the skin of the—

    1. Mouth? _____

    2. Upper eyelids? _____

    3. External ear? _____

    4. Upper cheek? _____

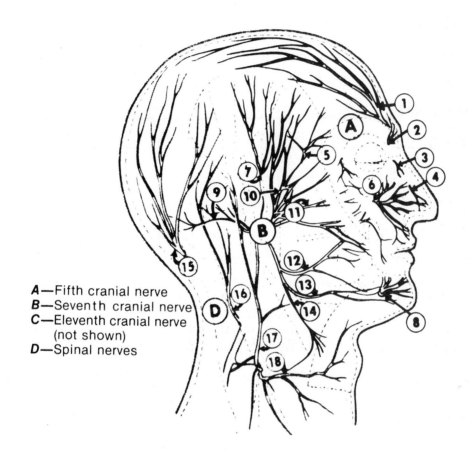

A—Fifth cranial nerve
B—Seventh cranial nerve
C—Eleventh cranial nerve
    (not shown)
D—Spinal nerves

12. Identify the names of the sensory and motor nerves shown on the diagram. Insert them in the spaces below.

    1. _____   10. _____

    2. _____   11. _____

    3. _____   12. _____

    4. _____   13. _____

    5. _____   14. _____

    6. _____   15. _____

    7. _____   16. _____

    8. _____   17. _____

    9. _____   18. _____

13. The facial nerve and its branches control the muscles of facial expression.

    a. By what other term is the facial nerve known? _____

    b. List the facial and scalp regions supplied by the temporal nerve.

        1. _____

        2. _____

        3. _____

        4. _____

        5. _____

    c. Which branch of the facial nerve supplies the muscles—

        1. Of the chin? _____

        2. Behind the ear?_____

        3. Of the mouth? _____

        4. Of the upper cheek? _____

14. The accessory and cervical nerves affect the regions of the head, neck, and back.

    a. The accessory nerve is also called the _____ cranial nerve.

    b. Name the nerve branch that affects the

        1. Scalp up to the top of the head _____

        2. Front and side of the neck, down to the breast bone_____

15. The nerves of the arm and hand are important to the cosmetologist in manicuring and massaging.

    a. Name the four principal nerves of the arm and hand.

        1. _____   3. _____

        2. _____   4. _____

    b. Which nerves supply the following parts of the arm and hand?

        1. Little finger side of the arm and palm of the hand_____

        2. Thumb side of the arm and back of the hand _____

        3. Fingers _____

    c. Identify the nerves in the diagram. *Insert the proper term in the space provided.*

        1. _____

        2. _____

        3. _____

        4. _____

Word Review

afferent	impulse	sensation
autonomic	motor	sensory
axon	neurons	sensory-motor
central	nucleus	spinal cord
cerebro-spinal	nutrition	spinal nerves
cranial nerves	peripheral	stimulation
dendrite	radial nerve	superficial
digital nerve	reflex	sympathetic
efferent	relaxation	ulnar nerve
fatigue		

Rapid Review Test

Date_____

Rating _____

Place the correct word in spaces provided in the sentences below.

12	mental	seventh
brain	motor	spinal
eleventh	neuron	sympathetic
fatigue	peripheral	trifacial

1. The cerebro-spinal nervous system consists of the spinal cord and the
   _____ .

2. The cerebro-spinal system controls all _____ activities.

3. Messages are carried to and from the cerebro-spinal nervous system by the
   _____ nervous system.

4. The autonomic nervous system is also called the _____ nervous system.

5. The structural unit of the nervous system is the _____ .

6. Afferent nerves are sensory nerves, and efferent nerves are _____ nerves.

7. Originating in the brain are _____ pairs of cranial nerves.

8. Excessive mental or muscular work can cause nerve _____ .

9. Controlling the motion of the face, scalp, neck, and ear is the _____ facial
   cranial nerve.

10. Nerves important in facial and scalp treatments are the fifth, seventh, and
    _____ cranial nerves.

11. The fifth cranial nerve is also known as the _____ nerve.

12. Originating in the spinal cord are the _____ nerves.

Date_____

Rating_____

Text Pages 70–75

TOPIC 5—CIRCULATORY (VASCULAR) SYSTEM

1. The circulatory or vascular system is vitally related to the maintenance of good health.

   a. What is the primary function of the vascular system?

   _____

   b. What are the two divisions of the vascular system?

   1. _____

   2. _____

   c. What are the four essential structures of the blood-vascular system?

   1. _____   3. _____

   2. _____   4. _____

   d. What are the two essential structures of the lymph-vascular system?

   1. _____

   2. _____

   e. From what substance is lymph derived? _____

2. The heart is an efficient pump.

   a. What is the function of the heart? _____

   b. What is the average size of the heart? _____

   c. What is the normal rate of heartbeat in an adult? _____

   d. What is the function of the heart valves? _____

   e. What is the function of the—

   1. Arteries? _____

   2. Veins? _____

   3. Capillaries? _____

   _____

f. Identify the parts of the heart.

1. _____
2. _____
3. _____
4. _____
5. _____
6. _____
7. _____
8. _____
9. _____
10. _____
11. _____
12. _____
13. _____
14. _____
15. _____

g. Which blood vessels fit the following descriptions?

1. Contain cuplike valves _____

2. Lie near the surface of the skin _____

3. Lie deeper in the tissues of the body_____

h. Name the two systems that comprise blood circulation.

1. _____

2. _____

i. Which system of blood circulation—

1. Goes from the heart to the lungs and back to the heart?

_____

2. Goes from the heart to all parts of the body and back to the heart?

_____

3. Human blood consists of plasma, red and white corpuscles, and blood platelets.

a. What part of the blood is plasma? _____

b. What part of the plasma is water? _____

c. What is the color of the blood in the—

1. Arteries _____   2. Veins _____

d. Name four essential materials that are carried by the blood to body cells.

1. _____

2. _____

3. _____

4. _____

e. Name two materials that are carried away by the blood from body cells for elimination.

1. _____

2. _____

f. List three additional important functions of the blood.

1. _____

2. _____

3. _____

4. The principal arteries of the head, face, and neck originate in the common carotid arteries.

a. What are the two divisions of the common carotid arteries?

1. _____

2. _____

b. Which division of the common carotid artery supplies the—

1. Brain? _____

2. Superficial parts of the head, face, and neck? _____

c. Identify the arteries shown in the diagram opposite. *Insert the proper term in the space provided.*

1. _____   12. _____

2. _____   13. _____

3. _____   14. _____

4. _____   15. _____

5. _____   16. _____

6. _____   17. _____

7. _____   18. _____

8. _____   19. _____

9. _____   20. _____

10. _____   21. _____

11. _____

d. Match the following arteries with their respective regions. *Insert the proper term in the space provided.*

facial   parietal   submental

frontal   posterior auricular   superior labial

occipital

1. _____ Crown and side of head

2. _____ Upper lip and septum of nose

3. _____ Forehead

4. _____ Scalp, back of ear

5. _____ Back of head

6. _____ Chin and lower lip

7. _____ Lower region of face

5. The blood returning from the head and face enters two principal veins leading to the heart.

   a. What are the names of the veins?

   1. _____   2. _____

   b. Where are these veins located? _____

6. Hand and arm massage is designed to improve circulation to these areas.

   a. Name the principal arteries that are below the elbow.

   1. _____   2. _____

43

b. Which artery is located on the thumb side of the arm? _____

c. Which artery is located on the little finger side of the arm? _____

d. Which blood vessels are located nearer to the surface of the arms and hands?

_____

e. Which blood vessels are located deeper in the tissues of the arms and hands?

_____

f. Two arteries are shown in the illustration. *Insert the proper term in the space provided.*

   1. _____

   2. _____

7. The lymphatic system acts as an aid to the venous system.

a. Name the four essential parts of the lymphatic system.

   1. _____

   2. _____

   3. _____

   4. _____

b. Describe lymph. _____

c. List three principal functions of lymph.

   1. _____

   2. _____

   3. _____

Word Review

angular	lymphatic	
anterior auricular	occipital	
aorta	osmosis	
artery	parietal	
auricular	pericardium	temporal
carotid	plasma	transverse facial
circulation	posterior auricular	vagus
frontal	submental	valve
inferior labial	superior labial	vascular
infra-orbital	supra-orbital	vein
jugular	sympathetic	ventricle
lymph	systemic	

Rapid Review Test

Date_____

Rating_____

Place the correct word in spaces provided in the sentences below.

arteries	filtration	parietal
atriums	forehead	pulmonary
bacteria	general	scalp
blood	heart	surface
capillaries	lungs	vascular
carotid	oxygen	ventricles
chest	parallel	water
deeper		

1. The circulatory system is also known as the _____ system.

2. The heart is located in the _____ cavity.

3. _____ connect the smaller arteries with the veins.

4. The pulmonary circulation is the blood traveling to and from the heart and _____ .

5. The red blood corpuscles carry _____ to the cells.

6. White blood cells destroy and devour harmful _____ .

7. Plasma consists mainly of _____ .

8. Lymph is derived from the plasma of the body by means of _____ .

9. The upper chambers of the heart are called _____ and the lower chambers are known as _____ .

10. Lymph reaches parts of the body not reached by the _____ .

11. Blood circulation that goes from the heart to the lungs is _____ circulation.

12. Blood circulation from the heart throughout the body and back to the heart is _____ circulation.

13. Vessels that carry blood from the heart to all parts of the body are called _____ .

14. The important veins are almost _____ with the arteries.

15. The veins and capillaries lie nearer the _____ of the body, whereas the _____ arteries lie in the tissues of the body.

16. The frontal artery supplies the _____ .

17. The _____ artery supplies the crown and side of the head.

18. The occipital artery supplies the _____ and back of the head.

19. The external division of the _____ artery supplies the various regions of the head and face.

20. The jugular veins return blood from the various parts of the head and face to the

_____ .

Date_____

Rating_____

Text Pages 75–77

TOPIC 6—OTHER BODY SYSTEMS

1. Glands are valuable organs necessary for the health and development of the body.
   a. Name two sets of glands of the body.

   1. _____

   2. _____

   b. What are two duct glands of the skin?

   1. _____

   2. _____

2. The excretory system eliminates waste products resulting from various cellular activities. Which organs eliminate the following waste products?

   a. Urine _____

   b. Bile pigments _____

   c. Semisolid food wastes _____

   d. Carbon dioxide _____

3. Respiration involves an exchange of gases in the lungs.
   a. Which gas is expelled during exhalation from the lungs?

   _____

   b. Into what does oxygen change food?_____

   c. What determines the rate of breathing of a person?

   _____

d. Why is nose-breathing preferable to mouth-breathing?

_____

_____

e. Why is deep abdominal breathing more beneficial than shallow breathing?

_____

4. The digestive system converts food into a form that can be used by the body.

a. In which organ is digestion—

1. Started? _____

2. Completed? _____

b. Which substances digest and process foods?_____

c. Nutrients are absorbed into the bloodstream through the _____

d. What happens to undigested food and waste?

_____

_____

Word Review

abdominal breathing	enzymes	oil glands
bile pigments	exhalation	organs
carbon dioxide	intestines	oxygen
colon	kidneys	sweat glands
digestive system	liver	urine
duct	mucous membranes	utilize
ductless	nasal passages	

Rapid Review Test

Date_____

Rating_____

Place the correct word in spaces provided in the sentences below.

duct	kidneys	muscular activity
energy	lungs	small intestine
enzymes	mouth	

1. The skin glands are _____ glands.

2. Urine is eliminated by the _____ .

3. Carbon dioxide is eliminated by the _____ .

4. Oxygen changes food into_____.

5. Energy expenditure and _____ determine the rate of breathing.

6. Digestion is started in the _____ and is completed in the _____.

7. Chemical changes are brought about by _____.

Physiology and Histology of the Skin

Date _____

Rating _____

Text Pages 80–84

TOPIC 1—STRUCTURE AND FUNCTION OF THE SKIN

1. A healthy skin has certain characteristics.

   a. What are two signs of a healthy skin?

      1. _____

      2. _____

   b. On which parts of the body is the skin the thickest and the thinnest?

      _____

2. Sensory nerve fibers in the skin react to which five separate sensations?

   a. _____   d. _____

   b. _____   e. _____

   c. _____

3. What substance helps to lubricate the skin and protect it from injury?

   _____

4. Generally hair grows over the entire body, with the exception of which areas?

   _____

5. Name two appendages associated with the skin.

   _____

6. Fingernails and toenails serve to protect the hands and feet.

   a. What kind of material composes fingernails and toenails? _____

   b. The technical term for the nail is _____ .

7. Each square inch (6.452 cm2) of skin is made up of cells, hairs, blood vessels, sensory apparatus, glands, and nerves. *Write the correct number under the illustration that corresponds with the descriptions listed.*

   1. 650 sweat glands

   2. 19,500 sensory cells at the ends of nerve fibers

   3. 1300 nerve endings to record pain

   4. 95-100 sebaceous glands

   5. 13 sensory apparatus for cold

   6. 9,500,000 cells

   7. 160-165 pressure apparatus for the perception of tactile stimuli

   8. 65 hairs

   9. 78 sensory apparatus for heat

   10. 19 yards (17 meters) of blood vessels

   11. 78 yards (70 meters) of nerves

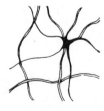

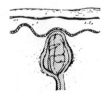

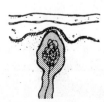

Word Review

corneum	melanin	sebum
dermis	pliability	sensation
epidermis	protection	stratum
keratin	sebaceous	tactile

Rapid Review Test

Date_____

Rating_____

Place the correct word in the spaces provided in the sentences below.

callous	epidermis	sebum
dermis	eyelids	texture

1. A healthy complexion has good color and _____ .

2. Continuous pressure on the skin may cause a _____ .

3. The skin is the thinnest on the _____ .

4. The two main divisions of the skin are the _____ and the

    _____ .

5. A function of _____ is to lubricate the skin.

Date_____

Rating_____

Text Pages 84–95

TOPIC 2—HISTOLOGY OF THE SKIN

1. The skin contains two clearly defined divisions, the dermis and the epidermis.

    a. Which division is the outer layer? _____

    b. Which division is the inner layer? _____

2. The epidermis is made up of many thin layers.

    a. How many layers are found in the epidermis? _____

    b. Name the epidermal layer that best fits each of the following descriptions:

        1. Contains a skin pigment_____

        2. Continually being shed and replaced _____

    3. Consists of transparent cells _____

    4. Is known as a granular layer _____

    5. Is known as the horny layer _____

3. The dermis of the skin contains two layers.

   a. Name them.

    1. _____

    2. _____

   b. Which dermal layer is directly beneath the epidermis? _____

   c. In which dermal layer are the following structures found?

    1. Sweat glands, oil glands, and hair follicles. _____

    2. Looped capillaries and tactile corpuscles. _____

4. The subcutaneous tissue is considered by some authorities as a continuation of the dermis.

   a. Where is the subcutaneous layer located? _____

   b. What are two other names for this layer?

    1. _____

    2. _____

5. Name three types of nerve fibers found in the skin.

   a. _____

   b. _____

   c. _____

6. The skin is indented with natural openings that are called _____ follicles with sebaceous (oil) glands and _____ of the sudoriferous (sweat) glands.

7. Approximately what percent of the skin is moisture? _____

8. To what is the pigment color of the skin attributed? _____

9. List five ways the skin functions as an organ of sensation and protection. The skin reacts to—

   a. _____   d. _____

   b. _____   e. _____

   c. _____

10. What is the general and constant internal temperature of a healthy body?

_____

11. Match the following definition. *Insert the proper term in the space provided.*

absorption   sebaceous   stratum germinativum
dermis   stratum corneum   subcutaneous
papillary layer

a. _____ Epidermal layer containing melanin

b. _____ Skin layer containing elastic fibers

c. _____ Fatty tissue of the skin

d. _____ Epidermal layer containing keratin

e. _____ Dermal layer containing tactile corpuscles

f. _____ Glands that secrete protective and lubricating oil

g. _____ Limited substances may enter the skin by this process

Word Review

absorption	epidermis	mucosum	sebaceous
adipose	excretion	papillary	sebum
corium	Fahrenheit	perspiration	secretion
corneum	fundus	pigment	sensation
corpuscle	germinativum	pliability	stratum
cuticle	granulosum	protection	subcutaneous
cutis	keratin	reticular	sudoriferous
dermis	lucidum	scarf skin	tactile
duct	melanin		

Structure of the Skin

1. From the following descriptive list of parts of the skin, identify the numbered parts on the illustration. *Insert the proper term in the space provided.*

adipose tissue   heat receptor   stratum germinativum

arrector pili muscle   pain receptor   sudoriferous duct

arteries   papilla   sudoriferous gland

capillaries   papillary layer   sweat pore

cold receptor   pressure receptor   touch receptor

epidermic scales   reticular layer   veins

hair shaft   sebaceous duct and gland

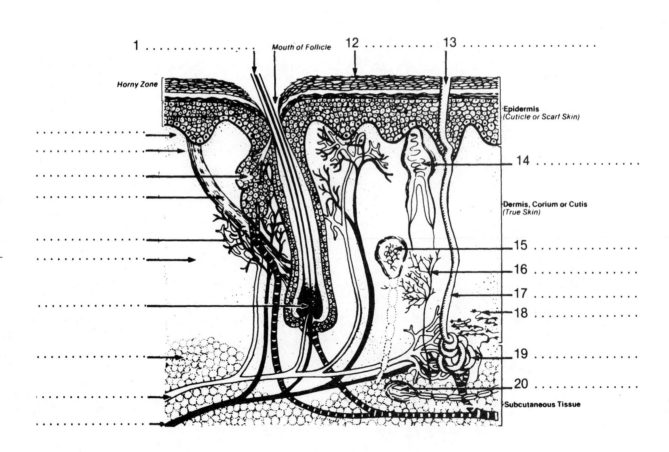

CHAPTER 7

Disorders of the Skin, Dermatology, and Special Esthetic Procedures

Date_____

Rating_____

Text Pages 97–103

TOPIC 1—UNDERSTANDING SKIN DISORDERS

1. Cosmetology and dermatology are services that ideally complement one another. The esthetician should be able to identify those skin disorders that may be treated in the salon and those that require medical attention. *Place the correct word in spaces provided in the sentences below.*

   a. _____ is the study of the skin, its function, its diseases, and its treatment.

   b. Pathology is the study of _____ .

   c. The study of the hair and its diseases is called _____ .

   d. _____ is the study of the causes of disease.

   e. The recognition of a disease from its symptoms is called a _____ .

   f. The term _____ is the foretelling of the probable course of a disease.

2. Following are additional definitions that refer to conditions of the skin. *Place the correct word in spaces provided in the sentences below.*

   a. Keratosis refers to a condition of the skin that involves _____ .

   b. Parakeratosis refers to nuclei in the cells of the _____ layer of the skin.

   c. Acanthosis is a condition that is the result of an increased number of prickle

   _____ .

d. "Dyskeratosis" refers to imperfect keratinazation of individual _____ cells.

e. A condition that produces a spongelike appearance of the skin is called

_____ .

f. "Pruitus" is the medical term for a skin condition that causes _____ and itching.

g. The medical term for redness of the skin is _____ .

h. The medical term for swelling is _____ .

i. When a condition is severe it is said to be _____ .

3. A lesion of the skin is a structural change in tissue caused by injury or disease.

   a. Name the characteristic primary lesion present in each of the following conditions.

      1. A discolored spot or patch _____

      2. A small dry elevated pimple _____

      3. An itchy, swollen lesion _____

      4. A solid lump larger than a papule_____

      5. An external swelling that varies in shape and color _____

      6. A _____ is a blister with clear fluid in it.

      7. A large blister containing a watery fluid similar to a vesicle _____ .

      8. An elevation of the skin that is inflamed and contains pus is a _____ .

4. Name the characteristic secondary lesions that develop in the later stages of a disease.

   a. A _____ is an accumulation of epidermal flakes, dry or greasy.

   b. A _____ is an accumulation of serum and pus mixed with other epidermal waste.

   c. A skin sore or abrasion caused by scratching or scraping the skin is called an

     _____ .

   d. A _____ is a crack in the skin such as is often caused by chapping.

   e. An _____ is an open lesion on the skin or mucous membrane, accompanied by pus.

   f. A _____ is likely to form after the healing of a skin injury or condition.

   g. A _____ is an abnormal discoloration of the skin.

5. Match the following definitions. Insert the proper term in the space provided.

acute disease	disease	parasitic
allergy	epidemic	pathogenic disease
chronic disease	infectious disease	seasonal disease
congenital disease	occupational disease	systemic disease
contagious disease		venereal disease

a. _____ Any departure from a normal state of health

b. _____ Influenced by weather or climate

c. _____ Caused by sensitivity to certain items or products

d. _____ Shorter but more violent

e. _____ Attacks a large number of people

f. _____ Longer in duration, usually mild

g. _____ Communicable by contact

h. _____ Related to employment

i. _____ Present in the infant at birth

j. _____ Caused by vegetable or animal parasites

k. _____ Caused by pathogenic bacteria

1. _____ Leads to overfunctioning of the internal glands

m. _____ Commonly acquired by sexual contact

n. _____ May be caused by contact with a contaminated person or object

Word Review

abrasion	excoriation	pustule
acute	fissure	scale
bulla	hives	scar
chronic	infectious	stain
congenital	inflammation	subjective
contagious	lesion	superficial
contaminated	macula	systemic
crust	objective	trichology
cyst	occupational	tubercle
dermatitis	papule	tumor
dermatologist	parasitic	ulcer
dermatology	pathogenic	venereal
diagnosis	pathology	vesicle
epidemic	pediculosis	wheal
etiology	prognosis	

Rapid Review Test

Date_____

Rating_____

Place the correct word in spaces provided in the sentences below.

abrasion   parasitic   subjective
congenital   scale   trichology
dermatology   secondary   wheal
occupational

1. Itching is an example of a _____ symptom.

2. The subject of _____ deals with diseases of the skin.

3. The subject of _____ deals with diseases that affect the hair.

4. An epidermal flake is the same as a _____ .

5. A disease that is present at the time of birth is called _____ .

6. An insect bite causes a lesion known as a _____ .

7. Working with harmful chemicals may cause an _____ disease.

8. The esthetician is concerned with both primary and _____ skin lesions.

9. Another name for excoriation is _____ .

10. Pediculosis and ringworm are examples of _____ diseases.

Date_____

Rating_____

Text Pages 103–108

TOPIC 2—DISORDERS OF THE SEBACEOUS (OIL) GLANDS

1. The common disorders of the sebaceous (oil) glands include whiteheads, blackheads seborrhea, and acne.

    a. What is the medical term for each of the following skin conditions?

       1. Blackheads _____

       2. Dry skin _____

       3. Whiteheads _____

       4. Oily skin _____

2. In cases of seborrhea, the sebaceous glands produce an excessive amount of oil.

   a. What is the appearance of the skin in this condition?

   _____

   b. On what parts of the body is seborrhea most frequently seen?

   _____

3. Acne is an inflammatory disorder of the skin involving the sebaceous glands.

   a. Is acne considered to be an acute or a chronic disease?

   _____

   b. On which three parts of the body does acne appear most frequently?

   1. _____

   2. _____

   3. _____

4. Rosacea is associated with excessive oiliness of the skin.

   a. Where does rosacea usually appear on the face?

   _____

   b. What are three characteristics of rosacea?

   1. _____

   2. _____

   3. _____

5. Steatoma (also called a "wen" or "sebaceous cyst") is a subcutaneous tumor of the sebaceous glands.

   a. Where does steatoma usually occur?

   _____

   b. What are the characteristics of steatoma?

   _____

6. Asteatosis is a condition of dry, scaly skin. What is generally thought to be the cause of asteatosis?

   _____

   _____

7. A furuncle is caused by bacteria that enter the skin through the hair follicles.

   a. What is the commonly used term for furuncle? _____

   b. What are the characteristics of a boil? _____

   _____

8. A cyst is a hard, painful lump regarded as a severe pimple that takes longer to reach the surface of the skin.

   a. What causes a cyst? _____

   _____

9. A pimple generally appears on the skin as an inflamed, red, or bluish lump.

   a. What happens within a follicle to cause a pimple?

   _____

   _____

   _____

   b. What is the danger of pinching and squeezing pimples?

   _____

   _____

   c. How does a whitehead (milia) differ from a pimple?

   _____

   _____

   d. Explain the differences between a blackhead (comedone), a whitehead (milia), and a pimple.

   _____

   _____

   _____

   _____

   e. Scars can result when severe cases of pimples and acne are not treated properly. What are the three types of scars that may result from pimples and acne?

   1. _____

   2. _____

   3. _____

10. Match the following skin conditions. Insert the proper term in the space provided.

   acne   comedones   seborrhea

   asteatosis   milia   steatoma

   a. _____ Infected pimples

   b. _____ Excessive discharge of sebum

   c. _____ Sebaceous cyst

   d. _____ Dry skin

   e. _____ Whiteheads

   f. _____ Blackheads

Word Review

acne	debris	raised
acute	furuncle	rosacea
asteatosis	hair follicle	sebaceous
blackheads	icepick	secretion
chronic	lesion	steatoma
clogged	milia	wen
comedones	pus	whiteheads
cyst	pustule	

Rapid Review Test

Date_____

Rating_____

Place the correct word in spaces provided in the sentences below.

adolescent	milia	sebaceous
alkalies	nose	seborrhea
asteatosis	rosacea	wen
comedones		

1. Blackheads are known as _____ .

2. Blackheads appear most frequently on the face, particularly on the _____ .

3. Asteatosis is a dry skin condition often caused by products containing

   _____ .

4. An oily, shiny condition of the scalp, nose, or forehead may be an indication of

   _____ .

5. Acne is more common during the _____ years.

6. Whiteheads are also known as _____ .

7. A chronic inflammatory disorder that affects the nose and cheeks is called

   _____ .

8. A steatoma is also called a _____ .

9. Acne is a chronic inflammatory disorder of the _____ gland.

10. A dry skin due to aging or bodily disorder is known as _____ .

Date _____

Rating _____

Text Pages 108–114

TOPIC 3—EXTRACTION OF BLACKHEADS AND OTHER BLEMISHES

1. One of the valued services an esthetician can perform is the extraction of blackheads and minor blemishes. Explain briefly the five basic steps for preparing the fingers for the extraction and cleansing procedure.

   a. _____

   b. _____

   c. _____

   d. _____

   e. _____

2. After the client's skin has been prepared, what are the three steps in the procedure for removing blemishes?

   a. _____

   b. _____

   c. _____

3. Whiteheads are overgrown with a thin layer of skin.

   a. How is the thin layer of skin broken in order to remove the whitehead?

   _____

   b. Why are the fingers preferred to a metal comedone extractor when extracting whiteheads, blackheads, and pimples?

   _____

   c. Why must pressure be controlled during the extraction of blemishes?

   _____

4. Before extracting pimples, they must be ripe or must have come to a head.

   a. Describe a pimple that is ripe or has come to a head.

   _____

   b. What should be done if the pimple is not ready for extraction?

   _____

   _____

5. Match the following definitions. *Insert the proper term in the space provided.*

| a deep cyst | discard | sanitary |
| astringent | lancets | sterilized |

a. _____ conditions must be observed when extracting blemishes.

b. _____ is used after extracting blemishes.

c. _____ is never lanced.

d. _____ items are used for extracting purposes.

e. _____ are used to open blemishes if they are ready for extraction.

f. _____ items used for the extraction of blemishes.

Word Review

abrasive	debris	parallel
astringent	discard	pimple
blackhead	disincrustation	pressure
cap of pus	Dr. Jacquet	sanitary
cartilage	extraction	saturated
cleansing	follicle	semiflexible
comedone	greasy	sterilize
comedone extractor	horizontal	vapor mist
cotton strips	irritating	vertical
cyst	lancet	whitehead
dead cell layer	moist towels	

Date_____

Rating_____

63

Text Pages 114–117

TOPIC 4—DISORDERS AND IMPERFECTIONS OF THE SKIN

1. Although the esthetician cannot treat disorders of the sudoriferous (sweat) glands, it is important to understand that these disorders can produce abnormal changes in the sweat production of the body. Which disorders are associated with the following:

a. Miliaria rubra _____

b. Bromidrosis _____

c. Hyperidrosis _____

d. Lack of perspiration _____

2. "Dermatitis" refers to an inflammatory condition of the skin. What two kinds of skin lesions are usually found in dermatitis?

a. _____

b. _____

3. Eczema is a form of dermatitis that should be treated by a physician. What are the three basic signs of eczema?

a. _____

b. _____

c. _____

4. Psoriasis is an unpleasant and disfiguring disease. What are the usual signs of psoriasis?

_____

5. Herpes simplex is a virus infection commonly identified as fever blisters. Where do the blisters usually appear?

_____

6. Occupational disorders of the skin are caused by an abnormal reaction to chemical or other harsh products. Which type of dermatitis may result from an allergy to cosmetic products or some cleaning agents?

_____

7. Abnormal conditions involving skin pigmentation may result from internal or external causes. Match the following definitions. *Insert the proper term in the space provided.*

albinism   lentigines   naevus   vitiligo
chloasma   leucoderma   suntan or sunburn

a. _____ Excessive exposure to the sun

b. _____ Small spots called freckles (usually red or yellow brown)

c. _____ Increased pigmentation commonly called "liver spots"

d. _____ Dark stain commonly called a "birthmark"

e. _____ Abnormal light patches on the skin

f. _____ Congenital condition of the skin when it lacks color pigment

g. _____ Acquired condition (leucoderma)that causes light patches on the skin

8. Hypertrophies are excessive or new growths on the skin. Match the following definitions. *Insert the proper term in the space provided.*

couperose   mole   verruca
keratoma   skin tag

a. _____ Round, thick patch commonly called a callous, usually on the palms of the hands or soles of the feet

b. _____ Small raised brown spot on the skin

c. _____ Commonly called a "wart"

d. _____ Breadlike fibrous tissue that grows out or away from the skin

e. _____ Condition characterized by broken capillaries

9. As a person ages, the deeper, or dermal, layers of the skin undergo changes. Describe briefly the characteristics of aging skin.

_____

_____

_____

Word Review

albinism	hyperidrosis	pigment
anidrosis	lentigines	psoriasis
birthmark	leucoderma	skin tags
bromidrosis	miliaria rubra	stain
chloasma	mole	sudoriferous
dermatitis	naevus	venenata
eczema	papules	verruca
herpes simplex	perspiration	vitiligo

Rapid Review Test

Date_____

Rating_____

Place the correct word in spaces provided in the sentences below.

albinism	elasticity	naevus
anidrosis	herpes simplex	prickly heat
bromidrosis	hyperidrosis	psoriasis
chloasma	keratoma	sudoriferous
couperose	lentigines	venenata
dermatitis	leucoderma	vitiligo
eczema	miliaria rubra	

1. When excessive sweating occurs, it is called _____ .

2. _____ is a condition commonly referred to as "liver spots."

3. The absence of melanin pigment in the body is called _____ .

4. _____ is a skin condition characterized by silvery scales.

5. Broken capillaries are called a _____ condition of the skin.

6. An aging skin often lacks _____ .

7. A birthmark is also referred to as a _____ .

8. A burning or itching sensation of the skin which may be caused by excessive heat is a sign of _____ .

9. When the body lacks perspiration, it is called _____ .

10. A matching cosmetic color will help the appearance in cases of _____ .

11. When perspiration has a strong, disagreeable order, the condition is called _____ .

12. A red, blistered, oozing area that may also itch may be _____ .

13. Prickly heat is also called _____ .

14. _____ is the medical term for various forms of lesions affecting the skin.

15. Occupational disorders such as dermatitis _____ may be caused by chemicals.

16. _____ is the medical term for freckles.

17. A callous is also described as _____ of the skin.

18. _____ refers to light patches or colorless areas of the skin.

19. The _____ glands are commonly called "sweat glands."

20. Fever blisters are often the sign of _____ .

Date_____

Rating_____

Text Pages 117–122

TOPIC 5—OTHER SERIOUS DISORDERS OF THE SKIN

1. The esthetician helps the client keep his or her skin clean and healthy. When a skin condition is obviously in need of medical treatment, it may be necessary to suggest to the client that he or she consult a physician.

   a. The least malignant and most common cancer is called basal cell _____ .

   b. The most serious skin cancer is called malignant _____ .

c. A _____ is an abnormal growth of swollen tissue that may be located on any part of the body.

d. Venereal diseases are associated with sexual activity and are characterized by _____ sores and rashes on the skin. However, sores and rashes are not always caused by venereal disease.

2. An allergy is a sensitivity that some persons develop to normally harmless substances. Which allergies are associated with the following descriptions? *Insert the proper term in the space provided.*

allergic dermatitis   dermatitis venenata   insect sting or bite

asthma   drug allergy   urticaria (hives)

dermatitis medicamentosis   hay fever

a. _____ Form of eczema caused by a variety of substances

b. _____ Causes a mild to severe reaction following a bite or sting

c. _____ Sneezing, coughing ... caused by plant pollen

d. _____ Characterized by symptoms that resemble a cold

e. _____ Inflamed breaking-out owing to allergy to food or drugs

f. _____ Occurs after an injection such as penicillin

g. _____ Medical term for dermatitis that occurs as the result of contact with chemicals, metal, etc.

h. _____ Allergic reaction to drugs or medication

3. An allergy is a sensitivity that may be characterized by various reactions. Name eight possible reactions a person may have to a substance.

a. _____   e. _____

b. _____   f. _____

c. _____   g. _____

d. _____   h. _____

4. Substances that cause allergic reactions are called "allergens." Match the following definitions. *Insert the proper term in the space provided.*

chemicals and polishes   dust and dirt   metal

cosmetics   medication   pollen

a. _____ Allergen found in the environment

b. _____ Allergen associated with plants and flowers

c. _____ Allergen in substances used on the skin

d. _____ Allergen associated with contact with implements

e. _____ Allergen associated with cleaning products

f. _____ Allergen associated with substances taken internally

5. The skin is capable of rapid regeneration and healing if it has been kept clean and healthy. The esthetician should be able to identify (but not treat) various types of wounds and skin imperfections in order to know when to suggest that the client consult a physician. Match the following definitions with the illustration that it correctly describes. *Insert the proper term in the space provided.*

abrasion	laceration	puncture
cyst	nodule	scar
fissure	polyp	ulcer
incision		

Word Review

abrasion	epidermis	polyp
allergy	fissure	puncture
asthma	gonorrhea	reaction
basal cell carcinoma	hay fever	regenerate
benign	hives	scar
cancer	incision	sensitivity
cyst	laceration	syphilis
degeneration	malignant melanoma	tumor
dermatitis	medicamentosa	ulcer
drugs	nodule	venenata
eczema	penicillin	venereal
environment	pollen	

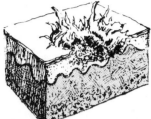

An

_____
is rough and red where the skin has been scraped or worn away

A

_____
is an uneven, jagged tear in the skin.

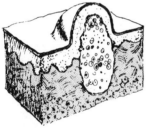

A

_____
is a mark left on the skin after the healing of a wound or sore.

A

_____
is a small knotlike node beneath the surface of the skin.

A

_____
wound is a hole in the skin made by piercing the skin with a sharp pointed object.

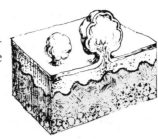

A

_____
is a growth that extends from the surface of the skin. They may also grow within the body.

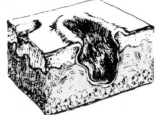

An

_____
is an open sore on the external or internal surface of the skin, often accompanied by the formation of pus.

A

_____
is a narrow opening or furrow in the skin.

An

_____
is a cut or incised wound, such as made with a knife or other sharp instrument.

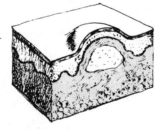

A

_____
is a saclike, elevated (usually round) area that contains a liquid or clear, semisolid substance.

CHAPTER 8

Chemistry for Estheticians

Date _____

Rating _____

Text Pages 123–131

TOPIC 1—UNDERSTANDING THE BASICS OF CHEMISTRY

1. A basic knowledge of chemistry helps the esthetician understand the composition and uses of cosmetics in the salon.

   a. Define "chemistry."

   _____

   _____

   b. Name two branches of chemistry.

   1. _____

   2. _____

   c. Which branch of chemistry deals with—

   1. Mineral substances? _____

   2. And vegetable substances? _____

   d. In what solvents are organic substances soluble?

   1. _____

   2. _____

   e. In what solvent are inorganic substances soluble? _____

2. Matter includes all substances which exist separately or in combination as a solid, liquid, or gas.

   a. What is matter? _____

   b. Name and give an example of the forms of matter having—

   1. A definite shape and volume _____

   Examples _____

2. Neither volume nor shape _____

   Example _____

3. Volume, but no definite shape _____

   Examples _____

3. An atom is the smallest part of an element having the characteristics of the element.

   a. What would happen to an atom of the element hydrogen if it were split?

   _____

   _____

   b. What is a molecule?

   _____

   _____

   c. What kind of atoms does a molecule of water contain?

   _____

4. Matter exists in the form of elements, compounds, and mixtures.

   a. What is an element? _____

   b. What is a compound? _____

   c. What is a mixture? _____

   _____

   d. Classify the following substances as either elements, compounds, or mixtures.

      1. Oxygen _____

      2. Iron oxide _____

      3. Concrete _____

      4. Air _____

5. Oxides, acids, bases, and salts constitute large groups of compounds in the study of chemistry. Which elements enter into the composition of—

   a. Oxides? _____

   b. Acids? _____

   c. Bases or alkalies? _____

   d. Salts? _____

   _____

6. Litmus paper is used to test and distinguish between an acid and a base.

   a. What is the test for an acid? _____

   b. What is the test for a base, or alkali? _____

7. Matter may be changed either physically or chemically.

   a. What happens to a substance when it is changed physically? Give an example.

   _____

   _____

   b. What happens when a substance is changed chemically? Give an example.

   _____

   _____

8. The properties of matter distinguish one form of matter from another.

   a. What two types of properties are used to describe matter?

   1. _____

   2. _____

   b. Name five physical properties of matter.

   1. _____

   2. _____

   3. _____

   4. _____

   5. _____

   c. Name two of the more widely known chemical properties.

   1. _____

   2. _____

9. Knowing the properties of some of the more common elements, compounds, and mixtures can help increase the effectiveness of an esthetician.

   a. How much oxygen is found in air? _____

   b. What are the characteristics of oxygen?

   _____

   _____

   c. Which oxygen compound has both antiseptic and bleaching properties?

   _____

10. A substance that readily gives up its oxygen is known as an "oxidizing agent."

    a. Give an example of an oxidizing agent. _____

    b. What happens to hair pigment when the oxygen is released?

    _____

    c. What is the process of taking oxygen away called? _____

    d. What is the substance that attracts oxygen called? _____

11. Nitrogen is a colorless, gaseous element found free in the air.

    a. What percentage of air is nitrogen? _____

    b. In what two forms is nitrogen chiefly found?

      1. _____

      2. _____

12. Pure water is essential to life and also plays an important role in the beauty salon.

    a. What are two methods for removing impurities from water?

      1. _____

      2. _____

    b. How can most microbic life be destroyed in water?

    _____

13. Soft water is preferred to hard water for use in a beauty salon.

    a. What substances are found in hard water?

    _____

    b. Why is hard water undesirable?

    _____

    c. How is hard water softened?

    _____

    _____

    d. How do you test water for softness?

    _____

    _____

    _____

14. The degree of acidity or alkalinity can be accurately determined by means of a pH meter.

    a. What do the following pH values mean?

      1. pH7 _____

      2. pH above 7 _____

      3. pH below 7 _____

    b. What pH range is desirable for cleansing lotions?

    _____

    c. What is the average pH of the skin mantle?

    _____

Word Review

acid	dilute	organic
air	element	oxide
alcohol	gaseous	oxidize
alkaline	gravity	oxygen
ammonia	hydrogen	pH
animal	hydrogen peroxide	pH meter
atoms	inorganic	rust
bases	iron oxide	salts
benzene	litmus paper	shape
chemistry	matter	soluble
combustion	minerals	solvent
composition	mixture	substances
compound	molecule	vegetable
concrete	nitrates	volume
density	nitrogen	

Date_____

Rating_____

Text Pages 131–135

TOPIC 2—CHEMISTRY AS APPLIED TO COSMETICS

1. Cosmetic chemistry is both a science and an art.

    a. What three areas of understanding of cosmetics are important to the esthetician?

    1. _____

    2. _____

    3. _____

    b. What are the four classifications into which cosmetics are divided?

    1. _____

    2. _____

    3. _____

    4. _____

2. A solution is a preparation made by dissolving a solid, liquid, or gaseous substance in another substance, usually liquid.

    a. What is a solute? _____

b. What is a solvent? _____

c. What substance is a universal solvent?

_____

d. What does the term "miscible" mean? Give an example.

_____

_____

e. What does "immiscible" mean? Give an example.

_____

_____

f. What is a dilute solution?

_____

g. What is a concentrated solution?

_____

h. What is a saturated solution?

_____

3. Colloids and liquid mixtures are immiscible materials in which the molecules stay separate.

a. Why is a thorough shaking required before using suspensions?

_____

b. What are the three steps in making suspensions?

1. _____
2. _____
3. _____

4. Emulsions are permanent mixtures of two or more immiscible substances united with the aid of a binder or emulsifier.

a. What is the usual appearance of emulsions?_____

b. What machine is used in the process of preparing an emulsion?

_____

c. What are the two classes of emulsions?

1. _____
2. _____

d. What are oil-in-water emulsions? _____

e. What is a water-in-oil emulsion? _____

f. Which of the two classes is thicker? _____

g. Give an example of an oil-in-water solution.

_____

h. Give an example of a water-in-oil solution.

_____

Word Review

colloidal mill	immiscible	solution
concentrated	insoluble	solvent
dilute	miscible	substance
emulsifier	mixture	suspensions
emulsion	saturated	
gums	solute	

Rapid Review Test

Date_____

Rating_____

Place the correct word in spaces provided in the sentences below.

ammonia	shaking	solute
dehydrated	soap	solvent
gums		

1. A dilute solution contains a small quantity of _____ in proportion to the _____ .

2. Suspensions separate upon standing and require a thorough _____ before being used.

3. Emulsions are permanent mixtures of oil and water combined with the aid of gums or _____ .

4. A mixture of a gas in water is _____ water.

5. Mucilages are thick liquids containing natural or synthetic _____ mixed with water.

6. When the skin is dry it is said to be _____ .

CHAPTER 9

Ingredient and Product Analysis

Date _____

Rating _____

Text Pages 136–140

TOPIC 1—PRODUCT FORMS

1. Products are available in dry or semidry, liquid, or semiliquid and gas forms. Give eight examples.

   a. _____

   b. _____

   c. _____

   d. _____

   e. _____

   f. _____

   g. _____

   h. _____

2. Each ingredient in a product plays a specific part. Insert the proper term in the space provided.

   antioxidants   fragrances   lubricants

   binders   humectants   preservatives

   emollients

   a. _____ Prevent damage due to oxidation.

   b. _____ Hold products together.

   c. _____ Soften and smooth the skin.

   d. _____ Give a characteristic odor.

   e. _____ Attract water.

   f. _____ Coat the skin and reduce friction.

   g. _____ Kill bacteria.

3. Cosmetics for body cleanliness help to maintain personal hygiene and good grooming.

   a. How do these cosmetics contribute to body cleanliness?

   _____

   b. Which kinds of cosmetics serve to improve body cleanliness?

   1. _____

   2. _____

   3. _____

   4. _____

   5. _____

   c. Which soaps are suitable for—

   1. Normal skin? _____

   2. Oily skin? _____

   3. Dry skin? _____

   d. Which soap is used mainly for laundry purposes? _____

4. Bath accessories are popular cosmetics because they increase the cleansing action and the beautifying benefits derived from the ordinary bath.

   a. Which cosmetics are used as bath accessories?

   1. _____

   2. _____

   3. _____

   4. _____

   b. Which bath accessories are used mainly after the bath?

   _____

5. Deodorants and antiperspirants are special cosmetics used to eliminate objectionable body odors.

   a. What is the function of a deodorant?

   _____

   b. What is the function of an antiperspirant?

   _____

   c. Name five types of deodorant and antiperspirant preparations.

   1. _____

   2. _____

   3. _____

   4. _____

   5. _____

6. Depilatories are sold in various forms for the temporary removal of superfluous hair.

   a. Name the various forms of depilatories.

   1. _____

   2. _____

   3. _____

   4. _____

   5. _____

   b. Which type of depilatory is generally used over the arms and legs?

   _____

   c. Which type of depilatory is preferred for the face?

   _____

Word Review

accessories	deodorants	medicated soap
active	depilatories	naphtha soap
alcohol	dusting powders	ointment
alkali	emollient	perspiration
antiperspirants	floating soap	shaving soap
astringent	glycerine	super-fatted soap
bath oils	green soap	superfluous
bath salts	hard-water soap	tincture
body oils	inactive	toilet soap
castile soap	ingredients	transparent soap

Rapid Review Test

Date_____

Rating_____

Insert the proper term in the space provided.

antiperspirants	hard	powder
astringent	medicated	salts
eggs	naphtha	super-fatted
face	oils	

1. Soap used for acne condition is usually _____ soap.

2. Do not use _____ soap on the face.

3. Coconut oil, washing soda, and sodium silicate may be present in a _____ water soap.

4. Lanolin or cocoa butter are ingredients of a _____ soap.

5. Bath _____ and _____ are used during the bath.

6. Body oils are used after the bath along with bath _____ .

7. Deodorants and _____ help to check disagreeable body odors.

8. An antiseptic and _____ are present in a deodorant solution.

9. The chemical type of depilatory has the odor of spoiled _____ .

10. The wax type of depilatory, being odorless, is preferred for the _____ .

Date _____

Rating _____

Text Pages 140–146

TOPIC 2—PRODUCTS FOR SKIN CARE AND COSMETICS

1. Cosmetic creams are either stable oil/water or water/oil emulsions. Name the six basic kinds of creams used in the facial salon.

   a. _____   d. _____

   b. _____   e. _____

   c. _____   f. _____

2. Emollient creams have lubricating and protective qualities and are used chiefly for the prevention of a dry skin. What are two other names for an emollient cream?

   a. _____   b. _____

3. Sunburn or sunscreen lotions either protect the skin against sunburn or relieve a sunburn.
   a. What is the active ingredient in a sunburn preventive lotion?

   _____

   b. What is the active ingredient in a sunburn remedial lotion?

   _____

4. Medicated lotions are advisable for the local treatment of skin disorders.
   a. Who is qualified to recommend medicated lotions?

   _____

   b. What are the basic active ingredients of medicated lotions?

   _____

5. A good face powder renders the skin soft and velvety, besides concealing blemishes and shine.

   a. Name six qualities of a good face powder.

   1. _____   4. _____

   2. _____   5. _____

   3. _____   6. _____

   b. Which quality imparts a smooth feel to the skin?

   _____

   c. Which ingredients cause the powder to adhere to the skin?

   _____

   d. Which ingredients give the powder an even spread?

   1. _____

   2. _____

   3. _____

6. When skillfully applied, the proper shade of makeup helps to improve the client's complexion and facial features.

   a. Which cosmetics are applied to the cheeks and lips?

   1. _____   2. _____

   b. In which four forms is cheekcolor available?

   1. _____   3. _____

   2. _____.   4. _____

   c. On what basis should cheekcolor be selected?

   _____

   d. On what basis should lipcolor be selected?

   _____

7. Harmless pigments or coloring agents impart varied shades to makeup cosmetics for the eyes. What is the function of mascara?

   _____

8. There are many products available for specific cosmetic purposes.

   a. Which makeup is suitable for theatrical purposes? _____

   b. In what two forms is cake makeup available? _____

   c. How is cake makeup applied?_____

   d. What benefits can be obtained from the use of a beauty clay?

   _____

Word Review

absorbency	eyebrow pencil	organic
adherency	eyeshadow	perfume
alkaline	face powder	petrolatum
antiseptic	glycerine	pigment
astringent	grease paint	potassium stearate
astringent cream	hormone cream	saturated
beauty clay	insoluble	skin freshener
beeswax	kaolin	solution
bloom	lipstick	sulfur
cake powder	liquid powder	suspension
cheekcolor	lubricate	talc
citric acid	lubricating cream	titanium dioxide
cleansing cream	makeup	tragacanth
cleansing lotion	mascara	ultraviolet rays
cold cream	medicated	vanishing cream
cream powder	mineral oil	zinc oxide
creams	moisturizing cream	zinc stearate
emollient cream	natural	
emulsion	ointment	

Rapid Review Test

Date_____

Rating _____

Insert the proper term in the space provided.

dry	membrane	suspension
emollient	oily	tragacanth
hormone	rouge	witch hazel
mascara		

1. A lotion that has an insoluble sediment at the bottom of the container is called a _____ .

2. A cream used for lubrication of the skin during massage is an _____ cream.

3. A liquefying cream is formulated to cleanse _____ skin.

4. A vanishing cream may be drying to a skin that is _____ .

5. The commonly known name for cheekcolor is _____ .

6. The mucous _____ of the inner lower lip is a guide to lipcolor selection.

7. A solution of alcohol and water that is known as _____ is used as a cooling lotion and mild astringent.

8. Three percent gum _____ is used to bind the substances to form cake powder.

9. The cosmetic used to darken eyebrows and lashes is called _____ .

10. A _____ cream is usually recommended for mature women with dry skin.

Date_____

Rating_____

Text Pages 146–150

TOPIC 3—LAWS GOVERNING COSMETICS MANUFACTURE

1. Manufacturers of cosmetics must follow certain rules and regulations in order to protect the consumer.

   a. What organization is responsible for enforcing laws that govern foods, drugs, and cosmetics? _____

   b. What does the Fair Packaging and Labeling Act do?

   _____

   _____

   c. How does labeling of products protect the public health?

   _____

   _____

2. Most cosmetics contain ingredients that can be bought at a grocery or drugstore. What is the danger of formulating your own cosmetics?

   _____

   _____

3. Millions of dollars in cosmetic products are sold every year, yet there are few complaints from consumers.

   a. To protect the client and the reputation of the salon, what should be done before applying a cosmetic to the client's skin?

   _____

   b. Where should complaints be sent, when necessary?

   _____

4. Organizations have been founded to protect the consumer by regulating advertising and false claims by manufacturers. What is the function of the Federal Trade Commission (FTC)? _____

5. What is the CTFA, and what does it do? _____

_____

_____

Word Review

allergies	formulas	labeling
commercially manufactured	fragrances	malpractice insurance
contamination	FTC	manufacturers
cosmetics	hypo-allergenic	preparations
Fair Packaging and Labeling Act	ingredients	products
FDA	irritations	reactions
		U.S. Department of Health

Nutrition and Health of the Skin

Date _____

Rating _____

Text Pages 151–158

TOPIC 1—NUTRITION AND THE HEALTH OF THE SKIN

1. Nutrition is the process by which food is assimilated and converted into tissue in living organisms. A healthy skin is dependent upon good nutrition.

   a. What is meant by malnutrition?

   _____

   _____

   b. Which body systems nourish the skin?

   _____

   c. How are the nutrients supplied to the skin?

   _____

   _____

   d. What is the name given to all body processes through which the living body utilizes oxygen and food in building up and breaking down tissues?

   _____

2. The three basic essential food groups are fats, carbohydrates, and proteins.

   a. Why are some fats important to the body?

   _____

   _____

   b. What is the most important carbohydrate?

   _____

c. Why is glucose important to the body?

_____

_____

d. Are sugars and starches proteins or carbohydrates?

_____

e. Proteins have been used in cosmetics since ancient times. What is the name of the protein used in cosmetics?

_____

f. What are the chief components of protein?

_____

g. Which foods provide an A-grade type of protein?

_____

3. Energy is measured in terms of calories.

a. What are calories?_____

b. What happens to calories that are not used by the body?

_____

_____

c. Is butter more fat or more protein? _____

d. What happens to the skin when weight is reduced too fast?

_____

_____

4. Match the following. *Insert the correct name of the organ or organs in the sentence that best describes the organ and its functions.*

colon   liver   pancreas

esophagus   mouth and salivary glands   stomach

intestines

a. _____ Principal functions are mastication and changing starch to sugar.

b. _____ Moves food along to the stomach.

c. _____ Bile acts as fat solvent and is associated with this organ.

d. _____ Manufactures gastric juices to aid digestion.

e. _____ Helps enzymes to act on fat, protein, and carbohydrates.

f. _____ Absorption of foodstuffs takes place here.

g. _____ Waste matter is moved to this area for elimination from the body.

5. Why are enzymes essential to body health? _____

_____

6. Nutrition information has been added to food labels by many food processors.

a. In addition to the name of the product, what else is listed on the label?

1. _____

2. _____

3. _____

b. When vitamins are listed on a label, what do the letters "RDA" mean?

_____

7. A balanced diet is essential to the health of the entire body and particularly the skin. All vitamins are utilized by the body, but some vitamins are more essential than others for different parts of the body. Match the following. Insert the proper vitamin in the space provided
to best describe its importance.

Vitamins

A	D	K
B	E	P
C		

a. _____ Severe deficiency of this vitamin may cause night blindness and
skin problems.

b. _____ Important for a healthy nervous system and the skin. Helps to
prevent beri-beri.

c. _____ Important to the clotting of blood and to proper functioning of
the liver.

d. _____ Helps to keep capillaries healthy and to prevent couperose condition from developing.

e. _____ Necessary for the health of connective tissue and formation of red
blood cells. A lack of this vitamin may lead to poor skin, scurvy,
and slow healing.

f. _____ Helps to develop and maintain healthy teeth and bones. Often
called "the sunshine vitamin."

g. _____ Lack of this vitamin may lead to liver and kidney problems and
anemia. This vitamin is essential for healthy skin and is sometimes included in cosmetics.

8. Vitamins are more abundant in some food than in others. List two or more natural foods
that contain an abundance of the following vitamins.

a. Vitamin A _____

b. Vitamin B _____

c. Vitamin C _____

d. Vitamin D _____

e. Vitamin E _____

f. Vitamin K _____

g. Vitamin P _____

Word Review

absorption	environment	nutrients
amino acids	enzymes	nutrition
anemia	esophagus	organisms
assimilate	fats	pancreas
balanced diet	food groups	peptide (end bonds)
beri-beri	food labels	polypeptides
body processes	gastric juice	protein
calories	glucose	RDA
capillaries	intestines	salivary glands
carbohydrates	liver	scurvy
circulatory system	lymphatic system	sebum
collagen	malnutrition	starch
colon	metabolism	stomach
connective tissue	minerals	toxic effects
deficiency	molecules	toxicity
digestive cycle	night blindness	vitamins

Date_____

Rating_____

Text Pages 159–166

TOPIC 2—NUTRITION AND THE EFFECTS OF MALNUTRITION

1. Water may not be thought of as an element of nutrition, but it is essential to the health of the skin and to efficient functioning of the entire body.

   a. Approximately how much of the body is made up of water? _____

   b. Name at least four ways water helps to keep the body healthy.

      1. _____

      2. _____

3. _____

4. _____

5. _____

2. The professional esthetician is concerned with the client's total health, but the main concern is the study of nutrition and its effects on the skin.

   a. Why is a well balanced diet essential to the health and beauty of the skin?

   _____

   _____

   b. What changes in the skin may be an indication of nutritional deficiency?

   _____

   c. Pellagra is a skin disease characterized by a skin rash. What dietary lack is associated with pellagra?

   _____

   d. Severe protein and calorie deficiency causes a yellowish cast to the skin. What is this condition called? _____

3. Hormones are sometimes added to skin creams.

   a. What are hormones?

   _____

   b. What are the two female hormones?

      1. _____

      2. _____

4. Studies have shown that tobacco, alcohol, and drugs can be harmful to the skin if they are used excessively.

   a. How does the excessive use of tobacco affect the skin?

   _____

   b. How does the excessive intake of alcohol affect the skin?

   _____

   _____

   c. How are drugs harmful to the skin?

   _____

   _____

5. Nutrition is important to health and especially important to pregnant women.

   a. How important is good nutrition to an unborn child (fetus)?

   _____

   _____

b. What should the esthetician do if he or she notes a change in the condition or color of a client's skin?

_____

6. There are people who are allergic to certain foods.

   a. What are some symptoms of food allergy?

   _____

   b. How do you know which food or foods have caused the allergic reaction?

   _____

   _____

7. Authorities agree that taking vitamins into the body by way of good food is the best way to obtain proper nourishment for the skin. However, vitamins in skin care preparations may have some beneficial effect. What are some benefits of vitamins in creams and lotions when applied to the skin? _____

Word Review

alcohol	drugs	progesterone
allergies	estrogen	scurvy
anemia	hormone	skin lesions
calorie	jaundice	symptoms
chemical imbalance	malnutrition	temperature
cholesterol	mental health	tobacco
dehydrate	nutrition	vitamin deficiency
dermatitis	pellagra	water

Date_____

Rating_____

Text Pages 166–170

TOPIC 3—METRICS FOR THE ESTHETICIAN

1. Nutrition labeling provides consumers with information about a product's ingredients, and these ingredients are listed in metric measures. Since the esthetician often recommends products, he or she should know the basics of the metric system. There are seven basic units for different types of measurements. All other SI (International System of Units) are derived from these seven units. Match the following. *Insert the proper term in the space provided.*

ampere	kilogram	mole
candela	meter	second
Kelvin		

a. _____ Unit of length

b. _____ Unit of mass

c. _____ Unit of temperature

d. _____ Unit of time

e. _____ Unit of electrical current

f. _____ Unit of light intensity

g. _____ Unit of amount of substance

2. When you know the number of teaspoons and multiply by a certain number, you will find the equivalent in the metric measure milliliters. If you have one teaspoonful (60 drops of liquid) and multiply by five, you will find that you have _____ millileters in metric measure.

3. Water boils at 212° Fahrenheit and at _____ ° Celsius.

Word Review

commercially manufactured	formulas	manufacturers
consumers	ingredients	metric
cosmetics	labeling	products
FDA		

Client Consultation and Skin Analysis

Date _____

Rating _____

Text Pages 172–179

TOPIC 1—CONSULTATION AND SKIN ANALYSIS

1. The initial impression the client has of a salon and the people who are employed there will determine whether he or she will become a regular client.

   a. What type of atmosphere should be maintained at all times in a salon?

   _____

   b. Where should the consultation room be located in a salon?

   _____

   c. Why do some salons offer free consultations or facials when it is the sale of services and products that pays salaries and overhead?

   _____

2. When a client asks the cost of various skin care treatments, what should the esthetician do?

   _____

3. How is the client given assurance that the salon is staffed by competent and ethical estheticians?

   _____

4. A consultation card is used to record important information for the client's records.

   a. List the seven points of information that should appear on the consultation card.

   1. _____

   2. _____

3. _____

4. _____

5. _____

6. _____

7. _____

b. On the back of, or on another card, what other information should be listed?

_____

_____

5. The skin analysis is done to determine the condition of the skin and the treatment it requires.

a. Describe the four basic steps in the procedure for the skin analysis after sanitizing the hands.

1. _____

2. _____

3. _____

4. _____

b. What should the esthetician do if he or she detects a skin condition that appears to be a disease?

_____

_____

Word Review

abnormalities	credentials	medication
allergy	diagnose	pacemaker
analyze	examine	patch test
atmosphere	eyepads	procedure
bronzing	flakiness	sanitize
chapped	follicle	texture
condition	hydrated	toiletries
consultation	magnifying lamp	Wood's lamp

Rapid Review Test

Date_____

Rating_____

Insert the proper term in the space provided.

abnormalities   diagnose   pacemaker   Wood's

condition   follicle   sanitized

consultation   hydrating   texture

1. The purpose of the consultation is to determine the _____ of the client's skin.

2. The magnifying lamp or the _____ lamp is used to analyze the skin.

3. The _____ helps to establish the client's needs and desires.

4. The esthetician should not attempt to _____ or treat a skin disease.

5. The esthetician's hands should be _____ before the skin is analyzed.

6. During the skin analysis, the skin is stretched slightly to examine the size of the _____ .

7. Skin _____ or a diseased condition should be treated by a dermatologist.

8. A client with a heart condition such as wearing a _____ should not have treatments that include high-frequency or galvanic current.

9. The esthetician should note the _____ as well as the condition of the client's skin.

10. A man's skin may need emollient or _____ creams or lotions.

Date_____

Rating_____

Text Pages 179–185

TOPIC 2—CLASSIFICATION OF SKIN TYPES

1. During the analysis, the esthetician will determine the client's skin type. Therefore, it is important for the esthetician to be able to identify different skin types. Match the following. Insert the proper term in the space provided.

acne   dry   normal

combination   mature or aging   oily

couperose

a. _____ Skin in good condition with a sufficient supply of sebum and moisture

b. _____ Skin having both dry and oily areas

c. _____ Skin lacking oil or moisture or both

d. _____ Skin generally loose, wrinkled, or lined

e. _____ Skin identified by broken capillaries

f. _____ Skin with an overabundance of sebum

g. _____ Blemished skin

2. Facial treatments benefit all types of skins. Explain how facial treatments benefit the following skin types.

a. Normal skin _____

b. Oily skin_____

c. Dry skin _____

d. Mature (aging) skin _____

e. Couperose skin _____

_____

f. Acne skin _____

g. Combination skin _____

3. Complete the following sentences:

a. When cleansing an _____ skin, the main objective is to cleanse and remove excess oil and impurities from the follicles.

b. A _____ skin may age prematurely if exposed to too much sun, excessive steaming, and drying masks or packs.

c. An oil-dry skin lacks _____ .

d The surface of oily skin will often resemble the skin of an orange because the _____ are enlarged.

e. Acne is more common during _____ than at any other time of life.

f. Seborrhea is a functional disease of the _____ glands.

g. Rosacea is characterized by excessive _____ of the skin.

h. The _____ skin is characterized by two or more different conditions.

Word Review

acid mantle	elasticity	normalize
adolescence	environment	oil-dry skin
aging process	flakiness	pigmentation
capillaries	follicles	puberty
coarse	germ penetration	sebaceous
combination	hormone level	sebhorrea
couperose	hydrated	sebum
cystic acne	lubrication	senile
dehydrated	metabolism	T-zone
diminish	moisture-dry skin	taut
discoloration		

Date_____

Rating_____

Text Pages 185–188

TOPIC 3—DIFFERENCES IN LIGHT AND DARK SKINS

1. The esthetician should recognize some of the important differences in skins of persons of different ethnic origins.

    a. There are three major divisions of humankind that are associated with skin color. Name the three divisions and state the color associated with each division.

    1. _____

    2. _____

    3. _____

    b. What determines the darkness or lightness of human skin?

    _____

    c. Why must the esthetician be particularly observant when examining dark skin underneath the magnifying glass or Wood's lamp?

    _____

    _____

    d. Does dark skin generally have larger or smaller sebaceous glands than light skin?

    _____

    e. Are all dark skins oily?_____

f. Why is dark skin less prone to signs of aging than light skin?

_____

_____

g. Why are epidermabrasion and brushing treatments good for most dark skins?

_____

h. What is the characteristic texture of Asian skins? _____

Word Review

ashen	epidermabrasion	Oriental
Caucasoid	epidermis	pigment
dead surface cells	exfoliate	pigmentary granulations
disincrustation	keloids	ultraviolet radiation
Dr. Jacquet massage	Negroid	

Rapid Review Test

Date_____

Rating_____

Insert the proper term in the space provided.

flakes	less	pigmentary
keloids	lower	warts
larger	perspire	

1. People with dark skin usually have better heat tolerance than people with light skin, therefore they _____more.

2. Sebaceous glands may be more numerous and _____ in dark skin.

3. Dark skin _____ (exfoliates) more easily than light skin.

4. Dead surface cells that flake off dark skin contain _____ granulations.

5. Skin cancer is seen _____ frequently in black skin than in light skin.

6. Body temperature in persons with dark skin remains _____ than in persons with light skin when they are exposed to extreme heat.

7. _____ are practically nonexistent in persons with dark skins.

8. Round, thick scars called _____ are more common in persons with dark skin.

Date_____

Rating_____

Text Pages 188–192

TOPIC 4—ADVISING THE CLIENT

1. The sale of products benefits the salon and the client.

   a. How does the sale of products benefit the salon?

   _____

   b. Why should large containers of products not be sold to clients?

   _____

   _____

2. There are six steps in the cleansing procedure which the esthetician may demonstrate for the client. Briefly describe these six steps in the cleansing procedure.

   a. _____

   b. _____

   c. _____

   d. _____

   e. _____

   f. _____

3. The client will need to know how to take care of his or her skin between visits to the salon. The home cleansing routine or regimen is similar to the cleansing procedure done in the salon.

   a. When cleansing the face, what item is used in place of a face cloth?

   _____

   b. What is the benefit of the astringent or freshening lotion when used following the removal of cleansing lotion or cream?

   _____

   _____

   c. Why is night treatment cream or protective creams and fluids recommended for use after the cleanser and astringent?

   _____

   _____

4. Why is it better not to guarantee treatments? _____

_____

5. Why are refunds discouraged?_____

_____

6. Some clients may want to know why they are advised not to use soap on the face.

   a. How should the esthetician explain this?

   _____

   _____

   _____

   b. The average pH of the skin is 5.5; neutral pH is 7. What is the average pH (alkalinity) range of facial soaps?

   _____

7. Name three enemies of the skin that have become more common in recent years.

   a. _____

   b. _____

   c. _____

Word Review

acid mantle	evaporate	moisture-dry
acidity	formulated	oil-dry
alkalinity	guarantee	pH balance
chemicals	hexachiorophene	pollutants
compensate	maximum	preservatives
dehydrated	mercury	regimen
detergent	minimum	residue
emollient	misconception	synthetic

CHAPTER 12

Client Preparation and Draping

Date _____

Rating _____

Text Pages 194–203

TOPIC 1—PREPARATION FOR THE FACIAL TREATMENT

1. Correct procedures are important to giving facial treatments. The treatment area must be well organized, and the client must be made to feel at ease.

   a. Name the five categories of items or supplies that should be set out and made ready before the arrival of the client.

      1. _____

      2. _____

      3. _____

      4. _____

      5. _____

   b. When should you prepare cotton pads, eyepads, and compresses to be used during the facial treatment: _____

2. When the client is wearing valuable jewelry, where should it be placed during the facial treatment?

   _____

3. Several kinds of head drapes are used in salons to protect the hair of the client while the facial treatment is being given.

   a. Why are soft paper towels often preferred to cloth ones?

      _____

   b. What is the main consideration when draping the client's head with a towel?

      _____

4. Cotton compresses, pads, and eyepads are an essential part of the esthetician's tools.

   a. Briefly describe the five steps in the preparation of cleansing pads and compresses.

   1. _____

   2. _____

   3. _____

   4. _____

   5. _____

   b. The cotton compress mask is made from a long (4 inches wide by 9 inches long) piece of beautician's cotton. How do you prepare a compress mask?

   _____

   _____

   _____

   _____

Word Review

apparatus	draping	salon gown
astringent	face chart	salon robe
cleansing cream	facial treatment	skin freshener
cleansing lotion	implements	spatulas
compresses	kimono style	sponges
containers	machines	supplies
cotton pads	preparation	tissue
cotton swabs	procedure	treatment cream
coverlet	protective fluids	valuables
dispensary		

Rapid Review Test

Date_____

Rating_____

Insert the proper term in the space provided.

beautician's	kimono or robe	salon gown
butterfly	organized	sanitized
covered	quiet	spatula
hurried		

1. A special kind of eyepad is called a _____ shape.

2. Products should be removed from containers with a _____ .

3. The professional esthetician should be well _____ at all times.

4. Facial movements should be done quickly without seeming _____ .

5. The facial treatment areas should be located in a _____ area of the salon.

6. Women clients should be provided with a _____ to wear during the treatment.

7. Male clients should be provided with a _____ to wear during the treatment.

8. Pads and compresses that are not used on the day they are made should be placed in a _____ container.

9. _____ cotton should be used to make cleansing pads and compresses.

10. The esthetician's hands should be _____ before beginning the facial treatment.

Cleansing the Skin

Date _____

Rating _____

Text Pages 205–222

TOPIC 1—CLEANSING THE SKIN AND REMOVAL OF THE CLEANSING PRODUCT

1. Once you have learned the facial cleansing procedure, you will be able to concentrate on efficiency of movement and lightness of touch. After studying the numbers on the facial chart in your text book, close the book and write the numbers in the correct areas on the face chart.

2. Although estheticians may vary their methods, it is best to master the standard procedures or those recommended by your instructor. *Insert the proper term in the space provided.*

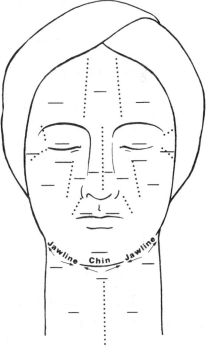

11	neck
12	pads
cleansing	pressure
lipcolor	sponges

mitts

a. When applying the _____ product, it is first applied to your fingers and then to the client's face.

b. When applying the product to the face, start by placing both hands, palms down, on the client's

_____ .

c. When applying cleansing cream or lotion to the face, your touch should be gentle, using only slight

_____ .

d. Cleansing lotion or cream is removed with cool, but not cold, cotton

_____ .

e. There are _____ basic steps to the procedure for applying cleansing cream or lotion.

f. Before starting the cleansing procedure on a female client, you should remove

_____ .

g. There are _____ basic steps in the cleansing procedure.

h. Following the cleansing routine with the cotton pads, the face is cleansed again with _____ made from the cotton pads.

i. The cleansing procedure may also be done with moistened _____ .

3. The use of a cotton compress mask is not a new practice, but remains a beneficial procedure in esthetics.

a. How many strips of cotton are usually needed to make a compress mask?

_____

b. The thinnest strip of cotton is molded to the client's neck. Where is the thickest piece of cotton used?

_____

c. What parts of the client's face must not be covered with the mask?

_____

d. What are the benefits of massaging over the cotton compress mask with an ice cube?

_____

Word Review

alternate	first finger	ring finger
circular movement	hyoid bone	rolling movement
cleansing mitts	lipcolor	rotate
cleansing pad	middle finger	simultaneous
compress mask	mold	sponges
downward movement	outward movement	stroking
eye makeup	patter	treatment
eyepads	pressure	upward movement
facial chart	reverse movement	water-soluble

CHAPTER 14

Techniques for Professional Massage

Date _____

Rating _____

Text Pages 224–240

TOPIC 1—TYPES OF MASSAGE

1. Facial treatments are given to help maintain the health and appearance of the facial skin. Name eight benefits of facial massage.

   a. _____

   b. _____

   c. _____

   d. _____

   e. _____

   f. _____

   g. _____

   h. _____

2. There are many types of massage, based on both body structure and body energy. Name the type of massage that matches each definition.

   a. _____ Manipulates deep muscle tissues.

   b. _____ Works with accupressure points.

   c. _____ Combines stretching of limbs with pressure on accupressure points.

   d. _____ Manipulates areas on the hands and feet.

   e. _____ Uses essential oils, which penetrate the skin during massage.

   f. _____ Uses gentle pressure to remove wastes.

3. A knowledge of neuromuscular anatomy is necessary in order to locate the areas overlying muscle motor points and the regions where motor nerves are sufficiently near the surface of the skin to be stimulated. *Insert the proper term in the space provided.*

Brachial plexus (Erb's point)

Cervical nerve

Facial nerve (buccal branch)

Facial nerve (main trunk)

Facial nerve (mandibular branch)

Facial nerve (temporal branch)

Trifacial nerve (mandibular division)

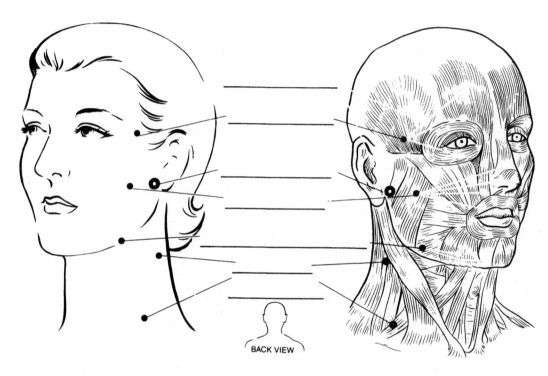

BACK VIEW

4. The esthetician should have hands that are well groomed, flexible, and relaxed. They should also be strong and supple.

a. Why should the esthetician practice exercise for controlled hand movements?

_____

_____

b. Name six practical practice methods designed to improve finger dexterity and supple hands.

1. _____

2. _____

3. _____

4. _____

5. _____

6. _____

5. Every massage treatment combines one or more of the basic movements. What three manipulations help to achieve the desired results?

a. _____

b. _____

c. _____

6. Manipulations used in massage are applied in a definite way and have particular purpose.

a. Name the massage movement given chiefly for its soothing and relaxing effects.

_____

b. Explain the correct positioning of the fingers for doing the stroking movement.

_____

_____

c. What is the main purpose of the petrissage movement?

_____

d. What is the purpose of the kneading movement in massage treatments?

_____

e. How do friction movements benefit the skin?

_____

f. On what part of the body are chucking, rolling, and wringing movements done?

_____

g. Describe tapotement or percussion movements.

_____

h. On which parts of the body are hacking and slapping movements done by the esthetician?

_____

i. Why are vibration or shaking movements done as part of a facial massage?

_____

7. Specific manipulations used and the number of times that each massage movement is repeated depend on desired effects.

a. How are rest and relaxation brought about?

_____

_____

b. How is stimulation brought about?

_____

_____

c. How is reduction brought about?

_____

8. Name eight tips for massage.

a. _____

b. _____

c. _____

d. _____

e. _____

f. _____

g. _____

h. _____

Word Review

activate	fulling	psychological life
categories	glandular activity	purpose
cell metabolism	hacking	relaxing effects
chucking	impurities	reverse
circulate	invigorate	rhythm
controlled pressure	kneading movement	rolling
coordination	manipulations	rotate
corrective	mannequin	secretions
cushions	massage	skin disorders
debris	massage techniques	slapping
digital stroking	muscle fiber	stimulate
direction of movement	nutrition	stroking
duration of movements	palmar stroking	subcutaneous tissue
effleurage	percussion	tapotement
environment	petrissage	tapping
excretion	positioning	texture
finger dexterity	practice methods	tone
flexible hands	premature aging	wig block
friction	preservative	wringing

Rapid Review Test

Date_____

Rating _____

Place the correct word in spaces provided in the sentences below.

calming	movements	position
circulation	muscles	tapping
friction	palm	toward
hacking	petrissage	wringing

1. Every facial massage combines one or more of the basic _____ .

2. When stroking large surfaces of the skin, such as the back and shoulders, the _____ may be used.

3. Light, slow, rhythmical movements have a _____ effect.

4. Massage movements are generally directed _____ the origin of the muscles.

5. Chucking, rolling, and _____ are variations of movements applied principally in massage of the arms.

6. _____movements, if done on the face, must be gentle.

7. Kneading movements give deep stimulation and improve the _____ of the blood to the skin.

8. The Dr. Jacquet and the _____ movements are alike and invigorate the area being treated.

9. When giving a treatment over a small area of the face, the fingers should be in a curled _____ so that only the cushions of the fingers touch the face.

10. Percussion movements include tapping, _____ , and slapping.

11. To obtain proper results from facial massage, the esthetician must have a thorough understanding of the nerves, _____ , and blood vessels.

12. Light, circular, _____ movements are usually done on the face and neck.

Date_____

Rating_____

Text Pages 241–250

TOPIC 2—MASSAGE 1, MASSAGE 2, AND DR. JACQUET MOVEMENTS

1. Massage 1 and massage 2 are made up of a sequence of movements that permit a smooth and graceful flow of one movement into another. Massage 1 involves cleansing and stimulation, while massage 2 involves deep penetration and relaxation.

    a. Describe the three main purposes of massage 1.

    1. _____

    2. _____

    3. _____

    b. Why are deep penetrating products not used in massage 1?

    _____

    c. What kind of cream is best for massage 1?

    _____

2. Once the esthetician has learned how to do all the basic massage movements, he or she will know which movement is most suitable for different parts of the face and neck. Select the movement or movements that match the name of the part or parts of the face or neck. *Insert the proper term in the space provided.*

    circular, sliding, very gentle tapping

    circular, tapping, scissor

    upward, circular, and criss-cross

    a. _____ Forehead

    b. _____ Around the eyes

    c. _____ On jawline and cheeks

3. Massage 2 is given with continuous and rhythmic movements. The main purpose of massage 2 is to aid in the deep penetration of treatment cream or lotions and to induce relaxation.

    a. Why is massage 1 given before massage 2?

    _____

    _____

    b. When is massage 2 omitted from a treatment?

    _____

    c. What kind of cream is applied to the face before massage 2?

    _____

4. The Dr. Jacquet movement is credited to Dr. Jacquet, a famous dermatologist.

    a. The Dr. Jacquet movement is recommended for what type of skin?

    _____

    b. When is the Dr. Jacquet movement not recommended?

    _____

    c. On what part of the face is the Dr. Jacquet movement not recommended?

    _____

Word Review

acne-blemished	massage 2	stimulating
criss-cross	oil ducts	tapotement
Dr. Jacquet	penetration	vapor
kneading	relaxing	variations
massage 1	scissor	

Rapid Review Test

Date_____

Rating_____

Insert the proper term in the space provided.

circular	index finger	ring finger
criss-cross	kneading	rolling movements
dead surface cells	massage 1	tapered
downward	massage 2	tapping movements
Dr. Jacquet	massage cream	upward strokes
eyelids	middle finger	vaporized
feathered off	petrissage	

1. The Dr. Jacquet movement uses the _____ manipulation.

2. An effective treatment for oily skin is the _____ movement.

3. Too much _____ can stretch the skin.

4. Movements should not be discontinued abruptly but should be _____ off.

5. _____ is effective for deep penetration of products.

6. _____ cleanses and prepares the skin.

7. Massage 1 removes _____ .

8. In massage 1, the skin is _____ or towel-steamed.

9. All massage movements done on the side of the neck are done with a _____ motion.

10. Massage 1 may be started with _____ on the forehead.

11. Piano or _____ are done on the cheeks.

12. The finger next to the little finger is called the _____ .

13. The _____ is between the ring and index fingers.

14. The _____ is next to the thumb.

15. When doing massage, hand pressure should go from firm to light until the hands are gradually _____ the face.

16. The petrissage movement should be done on the _____ .

17. _____ movements with the palms of the hands and thumb are done on the client's neck, chest, and shoulders.

18. Massage should not be done without the application of _____ .

19. In massage 1, _____ stroking movements are done on the forehead.

20. _____ (massage 2) may be done with the middle and ring fingers at the corners of the client's mouth.

Mask Therapy in Facial Treatments

Date _____

Rating _____

Text Pages 252–264

TOPIC 1—FACIAL MASKS

1. Clients like facial masks, and they are a popular salon treatment.

   a. What kind of sensation do masks usually produce on the skin?

   _____

   b. Name four benefits of facial masks.

   1. _____   3. _____

   2. _____   4. _____

   c. Is a mask used at the beginning or end of a facial cleansing procedure?

   _____

   d. What is the main benefit of a clay mask?

   _____

   _____

   e. How are masks classified? _____

   f. Name two kinds of gel masks.

   1. _____

   2. _____

   g. Why are commercial masks used in most salons?

   _____

2. Masks are made from a variety of ingredients, but some ingredients are known for different benefits. Name the main benefits to be derived from the following ingredients.

a. Glycerine _____

b. Zinc oxide _____

c. Calamine _____

d. Magnesium_____

e. Fuller's earth _____

f. Sulfur _____

3. Custom-made masks are generally left on the face for 10 or 15 minutes.

a. What is a custom-designed mask?

_____

b. Pectin is often used in gel masks. What is the main purpose of pectin?

_____

4. Theoretically, when vitamins are applied to the skin in a facial mask, they are said to bebeneficial.

a. What effects do the following vitamins produce when used in a facial mask?

1. Vitamin A _____

2. Vitamin C _____

3. Vitamin D _____

4. Vitamin E _____

b. Herbs are used in masks for their natural qualities. Which qualities are attributed to the following herbs?

1. Chamomile _____

2. Peppermint tea _____

3. Comfrey root tea _____

5. Certain ingredients used in facial masks may not cling or hold to the face.

a. How does the esthetician overcome this problem?

_____

b. When the mask has been left on the face for the required period of time, how is the gauze removed?

_____

6. Wax masks are favorites because they help to diminish fine lines and they moisturize dry skin.

a. In addition to the above benefits, what is the main purpose of the wax mask?

_____

b. What are the five steps in the procedure for the wax mask treatment?

1. _____

2. _____

3. _____

4. _____

5. _____

c. Why does the esthetician try to remove the wax mask from the client's face in one piece?

_____

_____

Word Review

absorb	gauze	plumps
acidic	gel	premixed
allantoin	glycerine	rose water
almond oil	gritty particles	soothing
calamine	herbal jelly	stimulating
calming	herbs	sulphur
clay	hydrating	teas
comfrey	ingredients	thyme
commercial	magnesium	toning
corneum layer	mask	vegetable
debris	menthol	vitamins
dehydrating	nontoxic	wax
egg mask	paraffin	witch hazel
formulas	pectin	yeast
fruit mask	peeling mask	yogurt mask
Fuller's earth	peppermint	zinc oxide

CHAPTER 16

Facial Treatments Without the Aid of Machines

Date _____

Rating _____

Text Pages 265–271

TOPIC 1—FACIALS FOR NORMAL, DRY, AND DEHYDRATED SKIN

1. The esthetician should be able to give facial treatments with or without the aid of machines.

   a. Name two reasons the esthetician may need or want to give facials without the aid of machines.

      1. _____

      2. _____

   b. Name six ways towel-steaming of the face may be beneficial.

      1. _____

      2. _____

      3. _____

      4. _____

      5. _____

      6. _____

   c. What size towel is recommended for facial steaming?

      _____

   d. What parts of the face are not covered during towel-steaming?

      _____

2. The procedure for a normal skin facial is completed in 15 steps.

   a. Name the steps.

     1. _____

     2. _____

     3. _____

     4. _____

     5. _____

     6. _____

     7. _____

     8. _____

     9. _____

    10. _____

    11. _____

    12. _____

    13. _____

    14. _____

    15. _____

   b. What is the difference between masks used for dry and for normal skins?

     _____

     _____

   c. What is a good alternative treatment for dry skin?

     _____

   d. How do the treatments for dry skin and aging skin differ?

     _____

Word Review

astringent	massage cream	sebum
combination skin	moisture-dry	spatula
dehydrated	normal	terrycloth
epidermabrasion	normal skin	towel-steaming
follicles	oil-dry	toxins
heat	oily skin	treatment cream
hydrated	penetrating cream	vaporizer
massage 1	protection fluid	wax mask
massage 2	sebaceous glands	

Date_____

Rating_____

Text Pages 271–283

TOPIC 2—FACIAL TREATMENTS FOR OILY, COMBINATION, AND PROBLEM-BLEMISHED SKIN

1. Oily and problem-blemished skins require special attention, the main goal being to help the skin function normally.

   a. Why is the Dr. Jacquet movement an important part of the treatment for oily skin?

   _____

   b. When giving a treatment for oily skin without the aid of machines, why are moist, warm towels used on the face?

   _____

   c. Which massage may be given for oily skin but is usually omitted?

   _____

2. Skin with dry and oily areas is called "combination skin."

   a. Describe the T-zone of combination skin.

   _____

   b. What is the difference between treatments for oily skin and combination skin?

   _____

   _____

   c. In a treatment for acne skin, why does the skin seem to worsen or flare up before it gets better?

   _____

3. When treating an acne condition, what is the esthetician's main objective?

   _____

   _____

4. Briefly list, in order, the 15 steps in the procedure for the special (strong acne) facial treatment.

   a. _____

   b. _____

   c. _____

   d. _____

   e. _____

f. _____

g. _____

h. _____

i. _____

j. _____

k. _____

1. _____

m. _____

n. _____

o. _____

5. For best results, the client should follow a strict home-care regime between salon treatments.

a. Why are home treatments necessary?

_____

_____

b. What must the client be told never to do when an acne condition exists?

_____

6. Disincrustation is an important part of the treatment for oily and problem-blemished skins.

a. What is disincrustation?

_____

b. If a commercial disincrustation lotion is not available, what can be used as a substitute?

_____

c. Why is the Dr. Jacquet massage movement usually performed following the removal of the disincrustation compresses?

_____

7. Couperose skin is skin that has broken capillaries.

a. What are the four rules that must be observed when treating couperose skin?

1. _____

2. _____

3. _____

4. _____

b. What is the purpose of the mask used on a couperose skin?

_____

8. Couperose skin will respond to salon treatments, but the client must also give the skin proper treatment between visits to the salon. Give six suggestions for the client's home-care regimen.

a. _____

b. _____

c. _____

d. _____

e. _____

f. _____

9. The epidermabrasion treatment should not be confused with dermabrasion, which deals with the deeper layers of the skin and must be done by a dermatologist.

a. What is epidermabrasion?

_____

_____

b. How does epidermabrasion benefit the skin?

_____

_____

_____

_____

10. Briefly describe the 10 steps in the procedure of the epidermabrasion treatment.

a. _____

b. _____

c. _____

d. _____

e. _____

f. _____

g. _____

h. _____

i. _____

j. _____

Word Review

astringent	emulsifies	mint tea
bicarbonate of soda	epidermabrasion	moisturizing
blood lancet	expel debris	normal
capillaries	extraction	oily
clogged pores	flareup	peeling
coltsfoot	hydrating	piano movements
commercial	ice cubes	problem-blemished
constriction	infectious	protection
couperose	infrared lamp	skin freshener
dermabrasion	kaolin powder	T-zone
dermatologist	massage 1	thinning
disincrustation	massage 2	vitamin P
distilled water	mild abrasive	yellow caps
Dr. Jacquet	mineral oil	zinc oxide

Multiple Choice or Selection Test

Date_____

Rating_____

Carefully read each statement. Underline the word or phrase which correctly completes the meaning of each statement.

1. The Dr. Jacquet movement is never done on

   a. combination skin

   b. blemished skin

   c. oily skin

   d. couperose areas

2. Astringent differs from skin freshening lotion because it

   a. is stronger

   b. is milder

   c. is more oil-based

   d. contains kaolin

3. Warm, moist towels are beneficial because they help to

   a. close the pores

   b. dry the skin

   c. open the pores

   d. prevent acne

4. The oil areas of the face are often referred to as the

   a. acne area

   b. T-zone

   c. combination zone

   d. hydrated zone

5. Combination skin has

   a. only blemished areas

   b. oily and dry areas

   c. cystic blackheads

   d. only hydrated areas

6. An acne condition may flare up or worsen before it

   a. gets better

   b. becomes couperose

   c. becomes cystic

   d. becomes allergic

7. Disincrustation is important because it

   a. supplies oil

   b. is astringent

   c. cures acne

   d. helps soften grease or dirt deposits

8. Broken capillaries are associated with

   a. normal skin

   b. couperose skin

   c. hives

   d. vitamin E

9. Epidermabrasion is associated with

   a. peeling or thinning surface layers of the skin

   b. vitamin P absorption

   c. removal of deep layers of skin

   d. home treatments for acne

10. A pimple may be extracted when it has

   a. become swollen

   b. a yellowish cap

   c. no yellow cap

   d. been squeezed

CHAPTER 17

Electricity, Machines, and Apparatus for Professional Skin Care

Date _____

Rating _____

Text Pages 284–300

TOPIC 1—ELECTRICITY—WHAT THE ESTHETICIAN SHOULD KNOW

1. Knowledge of the basics of electricity is important to the esthetician in order to operate machines and apparatus safely.

   a. What is electrical current?

   _____

   _____

   b. What is a conductor?

   _____

   _____

   c. What is the difference between direct current (dc) and alternating current (ac)?

   _____

   _____

   d. What is the difference between a converter and a rectifier?

   _____

   _____

   e. Describe an electrical circuit.

   _____

   _____

f. What is a fuse?

_____

2. Electrical measurements are expressed in terms of units.

   a. What is a volt? _____

   b. What is an ampere? _____

   c. What is an ohm? _____

3. An ampere is considered to be too strong, so the milliampere (1 /1000th of an ampere), is used for facial treatments.

   a. What is a milliamperemeter? _____

   _____

4. Match the following definitions. *Insert the proper term in the space provided.*

   electrode   plug   rheostat
   jack

   a. _____ Regulates the strength of the current used.

   b. _____ Serves as a conductor and applicator of electricity to area of the body.

   c. _____ Fitting device on the end of an electrical cord to be inserted into a receptacle on the apparatus.

   d. _____ Part of an electrical cord that connects the apparatus by inserting it into an electrical outlet or socket.

5. Certain precautions must be taken when a fuse is blown. Name the three safety precautions to observe when replacing a fuse.

   a. _____

   b. _____

   c. _____

6. Certain safety practices must be observed when using an electrically powered machine. In addition to the information about electricity from the previous lesson, you should also understand safety practices for connecting and disconnecting machines.

   a. How many plugs should be used in one outlet in a salon?

   _____

   b. What are the dangers of worn electrical cords?

   _____

   c. Why should you not remove a plug from an outlet by pulling on the cord?

   _____

d. When no electrician is on the premises during the time machines are in use, why is it important to know where fuse boxes are located and how to turn off the main switch?

_____

e. Name two items that should be kept in a salon where they can be found in case of emergency.

_____

7. Light therapy refers to facial or body treatments by means of light rays.

a. What are three types of light rays?

1. _____

2. _____

3. _____

b. How are therapeutic rays produced?

_____

c. Describe the benefits of ultraviolet rays.

_____

_____

d. Describe the benefits of infrared rays.

_____

_____

8. The three kinds of rays are either visible or invisible and comprise a certain percent of "sunshine."

a. State which rays are visible or invisible, and give the percent of sunshine for each type of ray.

1. Ultraviolet _____

2. Infrared _____

3. Visible rays _____

b. What are the dangers of overexposure to ultraviolet rays?

_____

_____

9. Color has long been used for its psychological value in creating moods or atmosphere. Name the moods or atmosphere associated with the following colors.

a. Red and yellow _____

b. Green and blue _____

Word Review

alternating current	fuse	ohm
ampere	high-frequency	plug
applicator	infrared	polarity changer
circuit	insulator	prism
conductor	invisible	rectifier
converter	jack	resistance
direct current	light therapy	rheostat
electrical outlet	low frequency	therapeutic
electricity	milliampere	ultraviolet
electrode	milliamperemeter	visible
flow	nonconductor	volt

Rapid Review Test

Date_____

Rating_____

Insert the proper term in the space provided.

alkaline	light	rheostat
amperage	milliamperemeter	spectrum
electrical circuits	negative	tanning
electrode	polarity	therapeutic
infrared	positive	ultraviolet
jack	prism	units

1. Electrical measurements are expressed in terms of _____ .

2. The _____ is an instrument used to measure the rate of flow of electrical current.

3. Cataphoresis is the use of the _____ pole to introduce an acid pH product, such as an astringent solution, into the skin.

4. Anaphoresis is the use of the _____ pole to force an alkaline pH product, such as a disincrustation lotion, into the skin.

5. An _____ solution dissolves grease deposits.

6. The _____ serves as a conductor and applicator of electricity to areas of the body.

7. The _____ regulates the strength of the current used.

8. A _____ is a fitting device at the end of an electrical cord.

9. _____ refers to having opposite poles in an electric current.

10. _____ refers to a unit of electrical strength.

11. Circuit breakers are commonly used devices for protecting _____ .

12. Treatments given by means of light rays are called _____ therapy.

13. Actinic rays are also called _____ rays.

14. If a ray of sunshine is passed through a _____ , it appears as the seven colors known as the rainbow.

15. A _____ lamp is an electrical apparatus capable of producing light rays.

16. Natural sunshine is composed of 80% _____ rays.

17. Ultraviolet rays are the shortest rays of the _____ .

18. Ultraviolet rays stimulate the production of pigmentation in the skin, which is called

_____ .

Date_____

Rating_____

Text Pages 300–323

TOPIC 2—MACHINES USED FOR PROFESSIONAL SKIN CARE TREATMENTS

1. The magnifying lamp provides magnification and glare-free light. Of what main benefit is the magnifying lamp?

_____

_____

2. The Wood's lamp is also used to analyze the skin.

a. What happens to different substances when exposed to the violet rays of the Wood's lamp?

_____

b. What color is normal, healthy skin when viewed under the Wood's lamp?

_____

c. When using the skin scope or the Wood's lamp, what safety precautions should be taken by the esthetician?

_____

_____

3. The facial vaporizer is one of the most important machines used in esthetics. Name seven benefits of this warm vapor mist.

   a. _____

   b. _____

   c. _____

   d. _____

   e. _____

   f. _____

   g. _____

4. The brushing machine is one of the most important machines used for professional facial treatments.

   a. What type of brush is recommended for delicate skin?

   _____

   b. What is the primary purpose of the brushing machine in facial treatments?

   _____

   c. Explain why the brushing procedure is not usually done on acne.

   _____

   d. On what type of skin is a faster brushing speed used?

   _____

5. The galvanic current is a constant and direct current rectified to a safe, low-voltage level.

   a. What are the two uses of galvanic current?

   1. _____

   2. _____

   b. Define "polarity."

   _____

   c. Why is it important to know which is the positive pole and which is the negative pole before applying galvanic current?

   _____

   _____

   d. List the four effects of the positive pole with galvanic current.

   1. _____

   2. _____

   3. _____

   4. _____

e. List the four effects of the negative pole with galvanic current.

1. _____

2. _____

3. _____

4. _____

6. Chemical solutions can be forced into the skin by means of a galvanic current.

a. What pole is used to introduce an acid pH stringent solution into the skin?

_____

b. What is the process called?

_____

c. What pole is used to introduce an alkaline pH solution into the skin?

_____

d. What is this process called?

_____

7. "Disincrustation" describes a process that softens and liquefies grease deposits that are accumulations of sebum in the follicles.

a. What kind of solution is used to penetrate the follicle and dissolve the grease deposits?

_____

b. During the disincrustation process, is the positive or negative pole held in the client's hand?

_____

c. For what type of skin is disincrustation usually recommended?

_____

d. Following the disincrustation step, what kind of movement is recommended for further extraction of excess oil and debris?

_____

8. Iontophoresis is the forcing of a treatment into the skin.

a. In the ionization process, which pole attracts an alkaline solution and which pole attracts an acid solution?

_____

_____

b. For ionization to work properly, what type of cream or lotion is used?

_____

_____

c. What are ionto rollers?

_____

d. One ionto roller is attached to the negative pole and the other to the positive pole. Which does the client hold?

_____

9. The esthetician often uses the galvanic machine for facial treatments.

a. What kind of mask is sometimes used with the galvanic machine?

_____

b. What kind of fruit is recommended for bleaching pigmentation spots with the use of galvanic current? _____

10. The high frequency current (Tesla current) is characterized by a high rate of oscillation.

a. What is the primary action of the Tesla current?

_____

b. Do the violet and orange rays produce the same benefits or different benefits?

_____

c. Name seven benefits of high-frequency (Tesla) current when used in a facial treatment.

1. _____

2. _____

3. _____

4. _____

5. _____

6. _____

7. _____

11. There are several different types of electrodes used in facial treatments.

a. Which type or shape is generally preferred for facial treatments?

_____

b. When applying high-frequency current to the face using facial electrodes, where are the movements started?

_____

12. Sparking is done by holding the electrode a fraction of an inch from the skin's surface.

a. What is the benefit of sparking? _____

b. When should high-frequency current be eliminated from the facial treatment?

_____

13. The vacuum-spray machine provides both suction for cleansing and spray for the application of treatment products.

a. What is the main function of the suction?

_____

b. What type of skin should suction not be used in?

_____

c. What happens when treating acne skin?

_____

d. What is the main purpose of the spray machine, also called an "atomizer"?

_____

e. In a facial treatment procedure, when is the spray usually used?

_____

f. What kind of liquid is used for the facial spray?

_____

g. How does the spray benefit the skin?

_____

14. The electric pulverizer produces a mist that is excellent for treating dehydrated, mature, and couperose skin. Name the two ways mist can be used.

a. _____

_____

b. _____

15. The carbonic gas spray is an atomizer that produces a high-powered spray.

a. What type of skin benefits most from the carbonic spray?

_____

b. What substance is used to recharge the carbonic gas spray tank?

_____

16. The electric mask is one of several methods used for deep penetration of products into the skin.

a. What type of product is usually used for dry skin for the electric mask treatment?

_____

b. What type of solution is used with the electric mask for treatment of oily skin?

_____

17. Treatment mitts are electronically warmed mitts used for extra-pampering hand treatments. Name three benefits.

a. _____

b. _____

c. _____

Word Review

absorption	distilled water	negative pole
acid	electric pulverizer	ozone
acid reaction	face cuvette	pacemaker
alkaline	fluorescent	pH factor
anaphoresis	galvanic current	pigmentation
apparatus	gauge	positive pole
astringent	germicidal	quartz electrode
atomizer	herb tea	skin scope
brushing machine	high-frequency	sodium bicarbonate
CO_2 spray	intensity of current	sparking
carbonic gas spray	ionization	spray machine
cataphoresis	ionto mask	treatment mitts
chemical solutions	ionto rollers	vacuum power
dehydration	machine	violet ray
disincrustation	magnifying lamp	Wood's lamp

Rapid Review Test

Date_____

Rating_____

Insert the proper term in the space provided.

acid	electric pulverizer	positive
acid mantle	electrode	prickling
alkaline	high-frequency	spray machine
brushing machine	ionization	suction machine
cuvette	ionto	thermal
disincrustation	negative	vaporizer
electric mask	pigmentation	violet ray

1. The purpose of the _____ is to slough off dead surface cells.

2. A _____ protects the client's body from spray during the vaporizing or spraying of the face.

3. The _____ is also called an "atomizer."

4. The spray rinses the skin and helps to restore the skin's _____ .

5. The main purpose of the _____ is to draw impurities from the pores.

6. Herb teas, plant extracts, and other ingredients are often used in the _____ .

7. The _____ is used to spray a fine mist over the face to soften dead surface cells and debris within the pores.

8. The _____ is one of several methods used to aid in deep penetration of products into the skin.

9. _____ is a process used to remove grease deposits from the skin.

10. An _____ solution is used to help dissolve grease deposits from the skin.

11. High-frequency current passes through electrodes to produce _____ .

12. The disincrustation solution is applied to a pad or sponge that is attached to the _____ pole.

13. The negative pole attracts an _____ solution.

14. The _____ process is the forcing of cream or solution into the skin.

15. An attachment sometimes used with the galvanic machine is the _____ mask.

16. When the _____ current passes through the electrodes, they light up with a violet light.

17. A quartz _____ is often used on acne prone skin.

18. The primary action of high-frequency current is _____ .

19. The juice of an orange may be used with galvanic current to bleach _____ spots on the skin.

20. During the process of disincrustation, the _____ pole is held in the client's hand.

21. When a client feels a slight _____ sensation, it means the current is strong enough.

CHAPTER 18

Facial Treatments with the Aid of Machines

Date _____

Rating _____

Text Pages 325–331

TOPIC 1—PROCEDURES FOR NORMAL, DRY, AND MATURE SKINS

1. Many salons feature treatments that require the use of machines. It is important to know how the machines are used for various facial treatments.

   a. How do machines aid the esthetician in giving facial treatments?

   _____

   b. Why should a person with normal skin have facial treatments?

   _____

   c. What is a good alternative treatment for normal skin?

   _____

2. There are three classifications for dry skin.

   a. Name the three classifications for dry skin.

   1. _____

   2. _____

   3. _____

   b. What is the main objective in treating a dry skin?

   _____

   _____

3. Four basic steps are included in all facial treatments that are done before beginning the actual treatment.

   a. Name the four preparation procedures.

   1. _____

2. _____

3. _____

4. _____

b. In the machine facial for dry skin, why is the vaporizer used at the beginning of the treatment?

_____

c. In the machine facial, deep penetration of products into the skin can be achieved by one of four different methods:

1. _____

2. _____

3. _____

4. _____

4. It is important that the esthetician memorize the steps for facial treatments in the order they are usually given. List the 19 steps in the procedure for giving a facial for dry skin with the aid of machines. Be brief.

a. _____

b. _____

c. _____

d. _____

e. _____

f. _____

g. _____

h. _____

i. _____

j. _____

k. _____

1. _____

m. _____

n. _____

o. _____

p. _____

q. _____

r. _____

s. _____

5. Mature men and women are concerned with keeping their skins youthful.

   a. What are the three main objectives when treating aging skin?

   1. _____

   2. _____

   3. _____

   b. What types of masks are recommended for aging skin?

   _____

Word Review

brushing	high-frequency current procedure	oil-dry skin
compress mask	lubricate	protective fluid
deep penetration	massage 1	sebum
dehydrated	massage 2	spray
disincrustation	massage cream	suction
electric mask	mature-aging	treatment cream
electric pulverizer spray	moisture-dry skin	vaporize
galvanic ionization	normal skin	wax mask

Rapid Review Test

Date_____

Rating_____

Insert the proper term in the space provided.

dehydrated	oil-dry	sebaceous glands
electric mask	protective fluid	sebum
moisture-dry	sanitize	vaporizer
normal		

1. After preparation of the client for a skin treatment, the esthetician should _____ his or her hands.

2. The _____ is used to open pores and soften dead surface cells.

3. Skin that is lacking moisture is called a _____ skin.

4. Skin lacking oil and moisture is dry or _____ skin.

5. Lack of _____ is the cause of oily dry skin.

6. Sebum (natural lubricant) for the skin is produced by the _____ .

7. The _____ is recommended as a method for deep penetration of products into the skin.

8. Following a facial treatment, _____ should be applied to the client's face and neck.

9. Skin that is functioning normally is called _____ skin.

10. Skin that has sluggish sebaceous glands is usually classified as _____ skin.

Date_____

Rating_____

Text Pages 332–343

TOPIC 2—PROCEDURES FOR OILY, COMBINATION, COUPEROSE, PROBLEM-BLEMISHED, AND ACNE SKINS

1. The problem with oily skin is that it attracts dirt, which can become trapped beneath the surface of the skin, where it can cause infection.

   a. Name two main objectives in the treatment for oily skin.

   1. _____

   2. _____

   b. Why does the treatment for oily or blemished skin take longer than for normal or dry skins?

   _____

   c. When giving a treatment for oily skin, name three ways deep penetration of products into the skin can be achieved.

   1. _____

   2. _____

   3. _____

2. The client with acne may require a series of treatments. What are the four main objectives when giving treatments for strong acne conditions?

   a. _____

   b. _____

   c. _____

   d. _____

3. It is important to know a step-by-step procedure for giving a facial treatment for oily or blemished skin. Test your memory by describing briefly the twenty-three steps usually recommended for the oily skin treatment.

   a. _____

b. _____

c. _____

d. _____

e. _____

f. _____

g. _____

h. _____

i. _____

j. _____

k. _____

l. _____

m. _____

n. _____

o. _____

p. _____

q. _____

r. _____

s. _____

t. _____

u. _____

v. _____

w. _____

4. When dealing with combination skin, each area of the face and neck must be treated for dry or oily areas.

a. If the client has an oily T-zone, what type of mask is recommended for the area?

_____

b. In the procedure for the facial treatment for combination skin, where is the disincrustation done on the face? _____

c. Name four ways deep penetration of products into the skin can be achieved when giving a treatment for combination skin.

1. _____

2. _____

3. _____

4. _____

5. When the client has a strong acne condition, it is important to begin a series of treatments that will not cause undue irritation but will be soothing to the skin. What are the four main objectives when giving a treatment for a strong acne condition?

a. _____

b. _____

c. _____

d. _____

6. To obtain results in clearing an acne condition, the client needs to follow a home-care regimen. Why is it important that only the esthetician extract blemishes?

_____

_____

7. In cases of infectious acne that are too extreme for salon treatments by the esthetician, what can be done?

_____

8. A couperose skin condition is usually found in thin, dry, delicate, and mature skins. The condition is characterized by weakening of the capillary walls. The esthetician must exercise great care and work with a light touch when giving a facial treatment for couperose skin.

a. Why should the client with couperose skin avoid extreme changes of temperature (hot and cold) on the skin?

_____

_____

b. Which vitamin, if ingested regularly, is said to be helpful in strengthening capillary walls?

_____

c. Why should the client with couperose skin be cautious of strongly spiced foods and alcoholic beverages?

_____

Word Review

acute	deep acidity	oily T-zone
blood lancet	extraction	regimen
capillary walls	flareup	spot suction
carbonic gas spray	galvanic ionization	strong acne
combination skin	germ penetration	treatment cream
couperose skin	infectious	vitamin P

Rapid Review Test

Date_____

Rating _____

Insert the proper term in the space provided.

acid mantle	extract	suction
couperose	germ penetration	tapping
deep penetration	massage 2	water-soluble
disincrustation	piano	wax
Dr. Jacquet movements	sebaceous glands	

1. The _____ mask is not used in the treatment for couperose skin.

2. The client with couperose skin may be given instructions on how to use the _____ movements at home.

3. Strong _____ is not done over extremely blemished areas of the skin.

4. Couperose skin is delicate; therefore, _____ movements are avoided.

5. Skin that has weak or broken capillaries is called _____ skin.

6. Washing the skin with harsh soap destroys its _____ .

7. Clogged pores can be caused by overactive _____ .

8. Galvanic ionization is one method for _____ of products into the skin.

9. When the acid mantle of the skin is washed away, the skin is vulnerable to _____ .

10. The Dr. Jacquet movements are done following _____ on oily areas of the skin.

11. In the treatment for acne, both massage 1 and _____ are eliminated.

12. The client should not attempt to _____ blemishes at home.

13. The _____ are helpful in removing excess oil from the skin and can be done gently on blemished areas, but not on strong acne areas.

14. When the treatment cream is _____ , a treatment mask may be applied directly over the cream.

CHAPTER 19

Removing Unwanted Hair

Date _____

Rating _____

Text Pages 344–359

TOPIC 1—ELECTROLYSIS AND OTHER METHODS OF REMOVING UNWANTED HAIR

1. The removal of superfluous hair is a service offered by most salons.

   a. What is the difference between temporary and permanent methods of hair removal?

   _____

   _____

   b. What two methods are most frequently used for permanent hair removal?

   _____

   c. What are three popular methods for temporary removal of superfluous hair?

   1. _____

   2. _____

   3. _____

   d. What temporary method is commonly used to shape eyebrows?

   _____

   e. To bleach or lessen the visibility of superfluous hair, what product is most commonly used?

   _____

2. A person who wants to practice electrolysis must be thoroughly trained in the most up-to-date methods.

   a. Which areas of the body may be treated for superfluous hair?

   _____

   b. Which areas of the body are not treated (except by a physician) for superfluous hair?

   _____

3. Wax hair removal treatments are popular salon services.

a. Why is the wax method for hair removal often preferred over shaving?

_____

b. Briefly describe the five steps in the application of liquid wax.

1. _____

2. _____

3. _____

4. _____

5. _____

4. Underarm hair is unwanted by most women.

a. Why is underarm hair removed in small sections rather than all at once?

_____

b. When the wax method is used to remove hair from the upper lip, in which direction is the fiber strip pulled, in the direction of or in the direction opposite to the hair growth?

_____

5. Wax should not be used when certain conditions exist. Name four conditions where wax would not be used on the skin.

a. _____

b. _____

c. _____

d. _____

Word Review

adhere	hair growth direction	shortwave
bonding	hair growth rate	skin test
diabetic	heredity	soft wax
diathermy	high-frequency	stubble hair texture
dielectric	hirsuties	superfluous
dormant hair	hirsutism	talcum powder
electrologist	hormone	temporary
electrolysis	hypertrichosis	thermolysis
epilation	lanugo (fine) hair	tweezing
fabric strip	muslin	virgin hair
follicle	papilla	wax method
galvanic multiple needle	permanent	wax pot
germinal matrix (hair root)	regrowth	witch hazel
growth angle	shaving	

Rapid Review Test

Date_____

Rating_____

Insert the proper term in the space provided.

depilatories	hirsutism	shortwave
electrolysis	hypertrichosis	superfluous
epilation	permanent	temporary
galvanic		

1. Unwanted and extra hair is called _____ hair.

2. _____ methods of hair removal destroy the hair papilla.

3. The method of permanent hair removal by electricity is called _____ .

4. With _____ methods of hair removal, repeated treatments are necessary.

5. The method of removing hair by the roots is called _____ .

6. Excessive growth of hair beyond what is normal is called _____ .

7. The presence of excess hair on areas where it is not normally grown is called

   _____ .

8. The _____ method destroys the hair by decomposing the papilla.

9. The _____ method destroys the hair by coagulating the papilla.

10. A popular group of temporary hair removers are called _____ .

CHAPTER 20

Enemies of the Skin, Aging Factors, and Cosmetic Surgery

Date _____

Rating _____

Text Pages 361–368

TOPIC 1—ENEMIES OF THE SKIN

1. The skin on the face and neck generally shows signs of age faster than skin on any other part of the body.

   a. Why is too much sun aging to the skin?

   _____

   _____

   b. What is the skin's main defense against the sun?

   _____

   c. For the skin to tan without harm to underlying tissues, how should you go about acquiring a tan?

   _____

2. Pollutants in the air can harm the skin.

   a. Name two ways the skin can be protected against pollutants.

   1. _____

   2. _____

   b. Why does the skin on the body remain younger-looking than the skin on the face and hands?

   _____

   _____

3. Excessive intake of alcohol is said to be damaging to the skin. How does the intake of alcohol over a period of time affect the skin?

   _____

4. Drugs may be harmful to the skin.

a. Why is it important to take only the drugs prescribed by a physician?

_____

_____

b. Why are some drugs bad for the skin?

_____

Word Review

alcohol	freckles	sulfuric acid
biological changes	gadgets	sun screen
drugs	overexposure	superficial layers
elasticity	patch test	tobacco
environment	pollution	tranquilizers
exaggerated	protective mechanism	weight loss

Date_____

Rating_____

Text Pages 368–392

TOPIC 2—THE THEORY OF PHYSIOGNOMY, COSMETIC SURGERY, AND DERMABRASION

1. Clients have their own ideas about what they consider to be attractive and how they want to look. It is important for the esthetician to be able to distinguish the relationship of one human facial feature to another, especially when advising women about makeup.

a. What is the ancient Greek theory of physiognomy?

_____

_____

b. Why did the Greeks establish a "canon" of beauty?

_____

_____

c. Why is appearance important to self image?

_____

d. Why is it unfair to teach that physical imperfections are an indication of personality defects?

_____

2. All living creatures go through a process of aging, from birth to death.

   a. How can premature aging of the skin be prevented to some degree?

   _____

   _____

   b. How does the loss of skin elasticity contribute to the appearance of aging?

   _____

   _____

3. Many people have cosmetic surgery done to improve their appearance. If the client's skin is oily before plastic (cosmetic) surgery, will the surgery change the condition of the skin?

   _____

   _____

4. Dermabrasion is a cosmetic surgery technique that must be done only by a qualified specialist.

   a. What is dermabrasion?

   _____

   _____

   b. What benefits are to be gained by dermabrasion?

   _____

   _____

   c. Why should sunlight be avoided for several months after dermabrasion?

   _____

   _____

5. The chemical peel (chemical skin refining) is often used as an alternative to dermabrasion.

   a. What is the difference in the procedure for dermabrasion and skin refining?

   _____

   _____

   b. What are the results of a successful skin peeling and refining treatment?

   _____

   c. When a serum is injected into lines and wrinkles, what kind of reaction occurs?

   _____

   _____

6. The esthetician does not perform surgery or give medical treatments, but he or she should understand what is involved in plastic (cosmetic) surgery and dermabrasion treatments.

a. Why should the esthetician have some knowledge of both preoperative and postoperative procedures? _____

_____

_____

_____

b. When the client comes to the salon for facial treatments following plastic surgery, what is the main concern of the esthetician?

_____

_____

7. Retin-A, the tradename for the drug tretinoin or retinoic acid, is a derivative of vitamin A.

a. Why was it originally developed? _____

b. Besides helping acne, how else does the patient's skin benefit from Retin-A?

_____

c. What benefit may Retin-A have as an anti-aging agent? _____

_____

d. What type of skin does it work best on? _____

e. How is Retin-A available? _____

f. As an esthetician, you cannot use Retin-A. What can you do?

_____

Word Review

anesthesia	heredity	rhinoplasty
antibiotic therapy	horizontal	rhytidectomy
augmentation	implant	self-image
blepharoplasty	incision	silicone
canon of beauty	malpractice	skin planing
cartilages	mucosa (nose lining)	subcutaneous tissue
caustic substance	naso-labial	submandibular lipectomy
chemical peel	oral surgery	superficial
congenital	physiognomy	surgical ink
criteria	postoperative	suture
dermabrasion	preoperative	symmetry
edema	psychological	toxic reaction
elasticity	reconstructive	vertical
ellipse (conic section)	rehabilitation	

Date_____

Rating_____

Insert the proper term in the space provided.

blepharoplasty   edema   rhytidectomy

chin   elasticity   surgeon

congenital   rhinoplasty

1. The technical or medical word for "facelift" is _____ .

2. The surgical correction of excess skin, pouches, and wrinkles around the eyes is called _____ .

3. The operation known as "submandibular lipectomy" is done to improve or correct the _____ .

4. Loss of _____ causes the skin to droop and deepens lines and folds.

5. Plastic surgery performed on the nose is called _____ .

6. Only a qualified _____ should give dermabrasion treatments.

7. Retention of fluid in the tissues is called _____ .

8. Conditions that are inherited or existing at birth are called _____ conditions.

CHAPTER 21

Male Skin Care and Grooming

Date _____

Rating _____

Text Pages 393–395

TOPIC 1—MEN'S SKIN

1. Men's attitude toward skin care, traditionally a women's service, is changing.

   a. Name two reasons for the change.

   1. _____

   2. _____

   b. What does servicing men mean for the esthetician?

   _____

2. There are few differences between men's skin and women's skin.

   a. Name five physical differences.

   1. _____

   2. _____

   3. _____

   4. _____

   5. _____

   b. Psychologically, men and women have different minds about skin care.

   1. Women tend to be more concerned with _____ and _____ .

   2. Men tend to be more concerned with _____ and _____ .

3. Men need to care for their skin no less than women do. Name four reasons why men need facials.

   a. _____

   b. _____

c. _____

d. _____

4. With male clients, what is the esthetician's first priority?

_____

Word Review

appearance	physical differences	scraping action
attitude	physiology	sebaceous glands
estrogen	psychological differences	sebum
health		

Rapid Review Test

Date_____

Rating_____

Insert the proper term in the space provided.

conditioned   performance   skin care

health

1. The esthetician must concentrate on _____ and _____ when selling to men.

2. Men have not been _____ to care for their skin.

3. It is important to show men that proper _____ is an effective and valuable aid to health and good grooming.

Date_____

Rating_____

Text Pages 395–398

TOPIC 2—SERVICES AND PRODUCTS FOR MEN

1. The esthetician can offer male clients virtually the same full range of services offered to women. Name six services offered to men and women.

a. _____

b. _____

c. _____

d. _____

e. _____

f. _____

2. Hair removal services can be offered to men.

   a. Name three forms of hair removal for men.

   1. _____

   2. _____

   3. _____

   b. Name five hair removal services for men.

   1. _____

   2. _____

   3. _____

   4. _____

   5. _____

3. For men to be comfortable in the salon, there needs to be a degree of privacy. Name two ways to offer this.

   a. _____

   b. _____

4. By and large, the same products can be used for male clients as are used for female clients.

   a. Name five products you can use for men or women.

   1. _____

   2. _____

   3. _____

   4. _____

   5. _____

   b. Name three products to stock for men only.

   1. _____

   2. _____

   3. _____

5. A number of companies manufacture skin care products formulated for men.

   a. Name four differences between men's and women's products. Men's products tend to be:

   1. _____

   2. _____

3. _____

4. _____

b. Why may it be profitable to stock men's skin care products?

_____

6. It's best to have your male clients shave before a facial treatment.

a. Name an advantage of this.

_____

b. What will you do if the client has a beard?

_____

7. All of the steps involved in deep pore cleansing will be virtually the same for men and women.

a. When using the vaporizer, what should you keep in mind?

_____

_____

b. Because men's skin tends to be oilier than women's, what two steps may be used more frequently?

1. _____

2. _____

c. What massage technique may be particularly useful for men?

_____

d. What types of masks are preferred for men?

_____

e. What properties are especially valuable?

_____

8. Name the five steps to a man's post-treatment consultation.

a. _____

b. _____

c. _____

d. _____

e. _____

Word Review

acid mantle	environment	performance
analysis	hospital gown	privacy
beard stubble	manual extraction	procedures
beard trimming	mask	products
Dr. Jacquet	moisturizing	vaporizer

Rapid Review Test

Date_____

Rating_____

Insert the proper term in the space provided.

analysis	patronized	shave
consultation	private	stimulating
feminized	relaxing	uncomfortable
fragrances	retail sales	unisex
moisturizers	rotary brush	

1. The atmosphere in the salon should be _____ in nature, to prevent intimidating male clients.

2. The male client should neither be _____ nor _____ .

3. It may be profitable to stock men's skin care products for _____ .

4. Have the client _____ before a facial treatment.

5. Education starts with _____ and _____ .

6. Conduct the consultation in as _____ an environment as possible.

7. The cleanser preferred for men's skin does not contain _____ .

8. If the skin is not smooth, the massage will be _____ for both the client and the esthetician.

9. _____ are a valuable addition to a man's skin, especially at the finish of a facial.

10. When using a _____ to work cleanser into the skin, the esthetician can use slightly heavier pressure than on women's skin.

11. Massage is _____ and _____ for a man.

CHAPTER 22

Esthetics and Aromatherapy

Date _____

Rating _____

Text Pages 399–406

TOPIC 1—ESTHETICS AND AROMATHERAPY

1. When essences and fragrances are used as part of a facial or body treatment, it is called "aromatherapy."

   a. Name two ways essential oils may be used in aromatherapy.

   1. _____

   2. _____

   b. What emotional states are brought about by aromatherapy?

   _____

2. In many ancient societies, herbs and fragrant oils were used. What were the three most important uses the ancients made of fragrant substances?

   a. _____

   b. _____

   c. _____

3. Seven terms help us identify different fragrances. Match the following definitions. *Insert the proper term in the space provided.*

   floral   fruity-blends   oriental

   floral bouquet   modern   spicy-blend

   forest-woodsy

   a. _____ Scent of one flower

   b. _____ Scent of more than one flower

   c. _____ Oils from fruit or herbs

   d. _____ Blend of herbs and plants

e. _____ Combination of various substances

f. _____ Blend of exotic spices and oils

g. _____ Combination of spices

4. Fragrant oils and essences must be extracted from various substances before they can be used in products.

   a. Match the following definitions. *Insert the proper term in the space provided.*

   distillation   expression   maceration

   enfleurage   extraction

   1. _____ Steam or boiling water used

   2. _____ Solvent penetration of plants

   3. _____ Pressing oils from substances

   4. _____ Fat spread on frames absorbs essential oils

   5. _____ Substances are plunged into hot oil which absorbs the essences

   b. Some animals provide products used in the manufacture of fragrances. Name four of these animals.

   1. _____

   2. _____

   3. _____

   4. _____

5. There are a large number of natural substances that are used in the manufacture of fragrances. Mainly, these substances are flowers, seeds, plants, fruits, woods, leaves, spices, and bark of trees. Name the substance you would expect to find in the following perfume or colognes.

   a. In a bouquet fragrance, the essential oils would come from _____ .

   b. In a spicy blend you would find substances from _____ .

   c. In lemon- or orange-scented products, _____ would be used.

   d. Leaves such as thyme, bay, and sage are _____ used to make certain fragrances.

   e. Sandalwood and cedar scents are taken from _____ .

   f. Caraway and almonds are _____ used in fragrances.

6. There are substances known for their therapeutic values. Name the main value attributed to the following substances. (For example, nutmeg and other spices are known for their agreeable odors.)

   a. Peppermint is considered _____ because it inhibits pathogenic bacteria.

   b. Comfrey root and alum root are known to be _____ because they contract tissue and reduce secretions.

c. Eucalyptus and wintergreen have _____ qualities.

d. Balm and comfrey root are calming and _____ .

e. Lemongrass and witch hazel are known to have exceptional _____ qualities.

f. Aloe and olive (oil from leaves) are used to soothe and _____ the skin.

g. Aloe, peppermint, and chamomile are known for their _____ qualities.

h. Since the skin needs moisture, rose leaves, orange blossoms, and rose hips are used for their _____ qualities.

Word Review

ambergris	extraction	natural
anesthetics	fixatives	Oriental
animal	floral	perfume
antiseptic	flowers	psyche
aromatherapy	forest	sachet
bark	fragrance	salicylic
bouquet	fruity	seeds
chlorophyll	herbs	solvent
cologne	incense	spicy
distillation	leaves	substance
enfleurage	maceration	synthetic
essences	modern	woods
expression	musk	woodsy

Rapid Review Test

Date_____

Rating_____

Place the correct word in spaces provided in the sentences below.

aromatherapy	expression	repulsive
chlorophyll	extraction	salicylic
distillation	floral	spices
enfleurage	maceration	therapeutic

1. When essences and fragrances are used in facial and body treatments, the procedure is called _____ .

2. Aromatherapy is considered to be a _____ technique that promotes relaxation and tranquillity.

3. If a fragrance represents only one flower, it is called a _____ scent.

4. Blends of _____ are used to create spicy and Oriental-type fragrances.

5. A person can become ill from _____ odors.

6. When essential oils are pressed out of substances, the procedure is called _____ .

7. When flower petals are plunged into hot fat to obtain their essential oils, the process is called _____ .

8. The use of solvents to obtain fragrances is called an _____ process.

9. When layers of flower petals or other substances are spread with fat to obtain fragrances, the process is called _____ .

10. When steam or boiling water is used to obtain fragrances, the process is called _____ .

11. The green coloring matter used in some cosmetic products is called _____ .

12. Wintergreen is used as an antiseptic because it contains _____ acid.

CHAPTER 23

Advanced Topics in Esthetics

Date _____

Rating _____

Text Pages 408–418

TOPIC 1—ADVANCED TOPICS IN ESTHETICS

1. Learning new techniques and technologies provides the esthetician with opportunities.

   a. Name two of these opportunities.

   1. _____   2. _____

   b. Why must the esthetician be familiar with new medical knowledge, even though he or she can't utilize this knowledge directly?

   _____

2. Phytotherapy is the use of herbs to treat various disorders.

   a. What's another name for phytotherapy? _____

   b. What part of the plant does herbal therapy use? _____

   c. Name three functions of herbs when used medicinally.

   1. _____

   2. _____

   3. _____

3. There are number of ways to prepare herbs. Match the preparation method to its definition. *Insert the proper term in the space provided.*

   decoctions   ointments   tinctures

   infusions   poultices

   a. _____ Made by steeping the herb in boiling water

   b. _____ Made by boiling the herb in water

c. _____ Made by soaking the herb in alcohol

d. _____ Made by crushing the herb and mixing it with a hot liquid to form a paste

e. _____ Made by mixing the herb with petroleum jelly to make a thick cream or salve

4. Why are poultices and ointments more effective than fomentations?

_____

5. Advanced massage techniques stimulate and detoxify major organs and nerve centers in the body. Name two of these techniques.

a. _____

b. _____

6. Reflexology is a system of massage that balances the inner organs of the body.

a. What part of the body do manipulations target? _____

b. What other part may also be massaged? _____

c. Define the theory of reflexology.

_____

_____

_____

d. The tips of the toes energize the_____ .

e. The heels energize the_____ .

f. Reflexology is an _____ -based form of massage.

g. Name five objectives of reflexology.

1. _____

2. _____

3. _____

4. _____

5. _____

h. The reflexology massage always starts on the _____ , which is the _____ pole.

i. It always ends on the _____ foot, which is the _____ pole.

j. Name two reasons creams and lotion should not be used during reflexology.

1. _____

2. _____

k. Who should not receive reflexology treatments?

_____

_____

7. Lymphatic drainage massage is a system of massage that helps move waste through the body, through the lymphatic system, to detoxify the body.

   a. Name the differences between lymphatic drainage massage and reflexology.

   _____

   _____

   b. How does the system work?

   _____

   _____

   c. How does the lymph from the lower extremities and left side of the body funnel into the bloodstream?

   _____

   _____

   d. Through what does the lymph from the upper part of the right side of the body funnel?

   _____

   _____

   e. Name four results of lymphatic drainage massage.

      1. _____

      2. _____

      3. _____

      4. _____

8. Water therapies can be grouped into thalassotherapy and balneotherapy treatments.

   a. What is the difference?

   _____

   _____

   b. In _____ , the client relaxes in a tub of hot water while jets of water and air bubbles massage her.

   c. In the _____ , the client stands in a shower while the therapist plays jets of hot water up and down the spine and the main lymphatic channels.

   d. _____ and _____ promote perspiration and increase elimination of toxins.

9. The esthetician may use some of the thalassotherapy techniques by utilizing various algae treatments.

a. Name five uses of algaes.

1. _____

2. _____

3. _____

4. _____

5. _____

b. Why do algae products provide good nutrition for the skin?

_____

10. Body wraps offer a variety of benefits.

a. Name five benefits of body wraps.

1. _____

2. _____

3. _____

4. _____

5. _____

b. What is the most commonly treated area? _____

c. What types of products are used for body wraps?

_____

d. What is the purpose of the plastic sheet?

_____

11. Cellulite gives the skin a bulgy, rough, orange-peel appearance.

a. What is cellulite?

_____

b. What causes this fat?

_____

c. How is it formed?

_____

_____

d. Many doctors believe cellulite is no different from regular fat and can only be removed by_____ .

e. In view of this controversy, what should the esthetician do?

_____

_____

_____

_____

Word Review

Accutane	fomentation	properties
active ingredient	herbs	reflexology
algae	hydrotherapy	saunas
balneotherapy	infusions	sciatic nerve
body wraps	lymph	Scotch hose
cellulite	lymph duct	side effects
claims	lymph nodes	sinuses
contour tapes	lymphatic drainage	steam bath
controversial	ointment	structure-based
decoctions	phytotherapy	thalassotherapy
detoxify	polar organism	thoracic duct
drug	poultice	tinctures
energy-based	pressure points	tub treatments
feel		

Rapid Review Test

Date_____

Rating_____

Insert the proper term in the space provided.

birth defects	infusions	rapid
communication	lotions	relax
creams	medical applications	series
detoxify	moderation	shellfish
fomentation	paste	woman's
imbalance		

1. There is a fine line between salon care and _____ .

2. Accutane, a sister drug to Retin-A, is known to induce _____ .

3. Herbs should be used in _____ .

4. Herb tests are _____ .

5. A _____ is made by soaking a towel in the liquid in which an herb has been steeped or boiled.

6. Disorders within the body block the flow of energy and cause an _____ .

7. With reflexology, as with any massage treatment, _____ is vital.

8. During reflexology, no massage _____ or _____ should be used.

9. It is better to conduct a _____ of reflexology treatments than to overdo a single treatment.

10. Lymph flow is not as _____ as blood flow.

11. Water therapies _____ and _____ the body.

12. In algae pack treatments, the algae is mixed with water to form a _____ .

13. With algae packs and body wraps, make sure the client is not allergic to _____ .

14. Cellulite is typically a _____ problem.

CHAPTER 24

Estheticians Working with Physicians

Date _____

Rating _____

Text Pages 420–426

TOPIC 1—ESTHETICIANS IN THE MEDICAL FIELD

1. The career path of the graduating esthetician has expanded beyond the traditional roles. Many estheticians are working closely with physicians.

   a. Name four ways an esthetician may assist in a medical practice.

   1. _____

   2. _____

   3. _____

   4. _____

   b. What expertise does an esthetician bring to the medical practice?

   _____

   _____

   c. How do estheticians and physicians differ in terms of educational background?

   _____

   _____

   _____

2. Dermatologists are physicians who specialize in diseases of the skin, and in treating diseases, injuries, and conditions that affect the skin, hair, and nails.

   a. What training is needed to become a board-certified dermatologist?

   _____

   _____

b. Who administers the boards for dermatology?

_____

c. Name two areas a dermatologist may specialize in.

1. _____

2. _____

3. Surgery is considered strictly cosmetic when it is performed solely for esthetic purposes, to make the patient look better.

a. What is the medical name for each of the surgical procedures?

1. _____

2. _____

3. _____

b. The word "plastic" comes from the Greek word that means: _____

4. Reconstructive surgery restores functions that have been lost or to allow normal function that was absent at birth.

a. Name four types of patients might require reconstructive surgery.

1. _____

2. _____

3. _____

4. _____

b. Name two ways an esthetician may assist a physician with a patient after reconstructive surgery.

1. _____

2. _____

Word Review

blepharoplasty	echymosis	rhinoplasty
burn survivors	edema	rhytidectomy
camouflage cosmetics	lymphatic drainage	trauma scars
cancer surgery	micrographic surgery	
cosmetic surgery	physicians	
deformities	plastic surgery	
dermatologic surgery	post-operative	
dermatologists	reconstructive surgery	

Date_____

Rating_____

Text Pages 427–433

TOPIC 2—ASSISTING IN THE CARE OF SKIN DISEASES

1. There are numerous indications for lymphatic drainage massage. It is very effective when used in conjunction with esthetic facial treatments in helping to maintain clean, toned, and healthy skin.

   a. Name four indications for dermatologic conditions.

      1. _____

      2. _____

      3. _____

      4. _____

   b. MLD is very beneficial for traumatic injuries that result in edema and echtmosis, making it particularly effective for post-surgical edema and hematoma. Name three other areas that would benefit from this treatment:

      1. _____

      2. _____

      3. _____

   c. What is the method of lymphatic drainage treatment that uses machine providing pulsed suction to expedite the lymph? _____

2. The role of the esthetician in a dermatoligist's practice may focus on helping patients with skin disease or problematic skin.

   a. Name seven treatments an esthetician may do in a dermatolgic setting.

      1. _____

      2. _____

      3. _____

      4. _____

      5. _____

      6. _____

      7. _____

   b. Name three acne treatments that may be utilized in a medical setting.

      1. _____

      2. _____

      3. _____

Rapid Review Test

Date_____

Rating_____

Insert the proper term in the space provided.

alphy hydroxy acids	many	tension
black	necrosis	topical antibiotics
blanched	nutrition	trauma
epithelize	pink	wound
Garamycin gauze	red	yellow
ischemia	swelling	

1. A _____ is a break in the continuity of soft part of the body structures caused by violence or _____ to tissues.

2. Hematomas or bruising can be _____ colors.

3. Dermis normally will take one week to _____ if cared for properly.

4. All wounds will initially appear _____ and may stay this color for several months, lightening to a soft _____ .

5. _____ indicates infection, and in some, but not all, cases _____ can mean dead tissue, or _____ .

6. Wounded skin may take on a _____ appearance, which could be the beginning stage of _____ , or delayed healing.

7. Blood supply may be compromised due to excess _____ , lack of good _____ or too much _____ applied to the skin.

8. _____ are used on superficial burns with a break in the epidermal layer.

9. Post-operatively, third-degree burns are dressed with _____ to prevent infection.

10. The Esthetic, Manufacturers and Distributors Alliance has established guidelines to ensure procedural consistency in the use of professional rinse-off, pulse applications of _____ for which product safety has been sustained.

Color Theory

Date _____

Rating _____

Text Pages 435–442

TOPIC 1—UNDERSTANDING THE BASIC PRINCIPLES OF COLOR

1. Anyone who applies and sells makeup or works in the beauty and fashion field should have some understanding of the basic principles of color.

   a. Primitive people associated white and yellow with daylight and black with night. What color represented blood, fire, and life to them?_____

   b. When people surround themselves with bright colors are they considered to be more reserved or more outgoing? _____

   c. What is the name of the most potent pigment responsible for color in the human skin, eyes, and hair? _____

   d. Which skin color contains the most pigmentation—light cream color or ebony?_____

2. The primary colors are red, yellow, and blue. All other colors are made from these.

   a. If you mix equal parts of blue with yellow, what color is produced? _____

   b. If you mix equal parts of red with yellow, what color is produced? _____

   c. If you mix equal parts of red with blue, what color is produced? _____

   d. How are secondary colors achieved? _____

   e. How are tertiary colors achieved? _____

3. Hue is color as the eyes perceive it. Red is seen as red. Therefore, we say the hue is red. Define the following terms:

   a. Value_____

   b. Intensity _____

   c. Shade _____

   d. Tint _____

4. Some terms are useful when describing various color harmonies. (For example "mono-chromatic" means "one color in varied shades or tints.") *Insert the proper term provided.*

   a. An _____ color scheme is achieved by the use of three colors that lie adjacent to each other on the color wheel.

   b. A _____ color scheme is a combination achieved by the use of three colors that lie at equal distances from each other on the color wheel.

   c. A _____ color scheme is achieved by the use of two colors that lie directly across from each other on the color wheel.

5. Colors create certain effects.

   a. If a bright color makes an area appear larger, then dark colors are said to recede, or make the area appear _____

   b. Colors reflect other colors. If the complexion has a great deal of underlying red tones and a red dress is worn, will the skin reflect more or less red? _____

   c. Colors steal color when placed side-by-side. Does the darker color make the lighter color appear lighter or darker? _____

   d. Colors have temperature and are said to be cool or warm. Is orange a cool or warm color? _____

   e. Are very light pastels considered to be warm or cool colors? _____

Word Review

advance	ebony	neutral	shade
albino	harmonious	Nordic	temperature
analogous	hue	pigment	tertiary
carotene	intensity	primary	tint
Caucasian	melanin	recede	triadic
color scheme	melanocytes	reflect	undertone
complementary	Mongoloid	secondary	value
coordination	monochromatic		

Rapid Review Test

Date_____

Rating_____

Place the correct word in spaces provided in the sentences below.

advance	intensified	recede	temperature
analogous	monochromatic	reflect	triadic
complementary	neutral	steal	undertone

1. When a color scheme is made up of the same color but in variations of lightness and darkness, it is called a _____ color scheme.

2. An _____ color scheme is achieved by using three colors that lie adjacent to each other on the color wheel.

3. A _____ color scheme is achieved by using three colors that lie at equal distances from each other on the color wheel.

4. Colors that lie directly opposite one another on the color wheel are _____ .

5. Bright colors _____ or make an area appear larger.

6. Dark colors _____ an area or make it appear smaller.

7. If bright blue is placed beside light blue, the bright color is said to _____ color, which makes the light color appear even lighter.

8. Red worn near a flushed (red) face will _____ more red into the face.

9. Colors are said to be warm or cool. This is the _____ of colors.

10. Black, white, and gray are _____ colors.

11. Colors may have an _____ .

12. Blue eyes can be _____ by wearing blue that is lighter than the color of the eyes.

Date_____

Rating_____

Text Pages 442–446

TOPIC 2—SELECTING COSMETIC COLORS

1. It is important to help the client select her most becoming cosmetic colors.

   a. Why is foundation color tested on the client's jawline and neck rather than on the wrist?

   _____

   b. Why is translucent powder generally recommended when a colored foundation is used on the face?

   _____

2. Poorly applied color on the eyebrows will detract from the beauty of the face.

   a. How can you learn to sketch natural-looking eyebrows with an eyebrow pencil before doing the client's eyebrows?

   _____

   _____

   b. Why are brown, black, and charcoal the most popular eyebrow pencil colors?

   _____

3. Lip color is a part of complete makeup application.

   a. What is the purpose of the liplining pencil?

   _____

   _____

   b. What is the purpose of eye makeup?

   _____

   c. Must lip and cheek color match?

   _____

Word Review

auburn	corrective	foundation	predominate
blusher	demarcation	garish	ruddiness
contour	emphasize	harmonize	titian
contrasts	eyeliner	olive	translucent
coordinate	florid	pigmentation	undertone

Rapid Review Test

Date_____

Rating _____

Insert the proper term in the space provided.

cameo	copper	gray	olive
cheek color	demarcation	harmonize	salt and pepper
color key 1	ebony	lip color	titian
color key 2	florid	minimized	translucent
contour	golden		

1. All the colors in a good makeup should _____ with the client's own natural coloring.

2. Powder that does not add color is called _____ .

3. When the client has auburn or red hair, a _____ red or red-brown eyebrow color may be used.

4. Foundation should be blended so no line of _____ is seen on the face or neck.

5. When the client has _____ hair, soft gray or charcoal may be the most natural looking eyebrow color.

6. When the bone above the eye protrudes, the space can be _____ with brown eyeshadow.

7. Very light skin is often referred to as a _____ skin.

8. A very dark skin is often referred to an _____ skin.

9. An _____ skin is brown with greenish undertones.

10. A _____ skin has an abundance of reddish undertones.

11. In _____ , the undertones of the skin are predominantly blue.

12. In _____ , the undertones of the skin are predominantly yellow.

13. Foundation with a soft beige tone will tone down too much red in a flushed or _____ complexion.

14. Makeup in light and dark shades is used to _____ areas of the face.

15. Nail polish and cheek color should coordinate with _____ .

16. A skin that has a yellowish undertone is often referred to as a _____ skin.

17. Hair that is a mixture of dark with gray is called _____ hair.

18. Lip color and _____ need not match, but they should harmonize.

CHAPTER 26

Professional Makeup Techniques

Date _____

Rating _____

Text Pages 448–478

TOPIC 1—PRINCIPLES OF MAKEUP ARTISTRY

1. It takes time, practice, and patience to become a makeup artist.

   a. Why should the makeup artist also have sales ability?

   _____

   _____

   b. What is the main purpose of makeup?

   _____

   _____

2. Professional people often display their credentials where clients can see them.

   a. Why should the professional esthetician and makeup artist display his or her credentials?

   _____

   _____

   b. Why is it important to have all items and the makeup area organized before the client arrives for her makeup application?

   _____

3. It is important to analyze the client's face shape and features before applying makeup.

   a. Name the seven basic shapes.

   1. _____

   2. _____

   3. _____

4. _____

5. _____

6. _____

7. _____

b. What is the usual width between normally set eyes?

_____

c. Why is it important to be able to shape the client's eyebrows as part of your makeup service?

_____

_____

d. Are eyebrows tweezed out in the direction of hair growth or in the opposite direction of the hair growth?

_____

4. The makeup base, or foundation, is one of the most important cosmetics used in a makeup application.

a. What are the two main benefits of foundation:

1. _____

2. _____

b. Why do makeup artists often prefer to apply foundation with a silk sponge?

_____

c. When selecting foundation colors, where is foundation tested to be sure it will blend well with the client's natural skin color?

_____

5. Many makeup artists are experts in corrective makeup application.

a. What is corrective makeup?

_____

_____

b. Why is powder pressed on rather than wiped on the face?

_____

c. What is the purpose of cheek color?

_____

d. Why do most makeup artists prefer using brushes for the application of most cosmetics?

_____

e. What are the two most common mistakes women make when applying makeup?

1. _____

2. _____

f. What is the purpose of eyeliner?

_____

g. Why is it important to use a spatula and lip brush when applying lip color?

_____

_____

Word Review

apex of the brow	diminish	fluorescent	pigment
corrective	dispensary	illusion	souffle
coverage	emphasize	incandescent	superficial
credentials	enhance	minimize	texture

Date_____

Rating_____

Text Pages 479–504

TOPIC 2—SPECIAL MAKEUP TECHNIQUES

1. Corrective makeup can work wonders in balancing the features of the face and in concealing imperfections.

    a. When a nose is too large or wide in proportion to other facial features, what makeup technique is used to make the nose appear smaller?

    _____

    _____

    b. What can be achieved by the use of a corrective cover stick or cover cream?

    _____

    _____

    c. Where is contour shading applied for a high cheekbone look?

    _____

2. The use of highlighting and shading can be done on various areas of the face. Which would you apply to correct the following?

    a. A small receding chin _____

    b. A wide, square jawline _____

    c. A long, heavy chin _____

    d. A prominent double chin _____

    e. Small, deep set eyes _____

3. When doing makeup on women with dark skin, it is important to select colors carefully.

   a. When selecting foundation for dark skin, on what part of the face do you test the color?

   _____

   b. Why should foundation for dark skin contain little or no titanium oxide?

   _____

   c. Which is more effective on dark skin, shading or highlighting?

   _____

   d. What kind of face powder is recommended for dark skins?

   _____

   e. Should the woman with dark skin wear only pastel lip color and eyecolors or can she use more vivid colors than a woman with very light skin?

   _____

   _____

4. Artificial eyelashes can be used effectively to enhance the beauty of the eyes.

   a. What are the two most common mistakes women make when they apply artificial lashes?

      1. _____

      2. _____

   b. What kind of adhesive is best for eyelash application?

   _____

   c. When giving a test to see if the client may be allergic to eyelash adhesive, where is the drop of adhesive applied, and how long should you wait to see if there is going to be an allergic reaction?

   _____

   _____

   _____

   d. How should artificial lashes be removed?

   _____

   _____

5. The makeup artist should strive to create the most becoming and individualized makeup possible for the client.

   a. In addition to a woman's personal coloring of hair, skin, and eyes, what else must be considered when you design a personalized makeup?

   _____

   _____

   b. Makeup artists do not always follow the same routine but use their creative imagination when designing a personalized makeup. As a beginner, why is it a good idea to practice a definite step-by-step procedure? _____

Word Review

45-degree angle	contrived	grotesque	radiance
accentuate	cover stick	inherited trait	slenderize
analine tint	emphasize	prominent	surgical adhesive
artificial	feather	proportion	titanium oxide
consistency	glamorous		

Rapid Review Test

Date_____

Rating_____

Place the correct word in spaces provided in the sentences below.

analine derivative	emphasize	prominent	surgical
consistency	feathered	spatula	titanium oxide

1. The right _____ of cake liner can be achieved by blending the moistened cosmetic on the ball of the thumb.

2. Lip color (stick) should never be applied directly from a container. It is more sanitary to use a _____ to take a small amount of the cosmetic from the container.

3. The best adhesive for artificial eyelashes is called _____ adhesive.

4. An _____ tint should never be used to darken eyelashes and eyebrows.

5. Light foundation is used to _____ a facial feature.

6. A large jaw will appear less _____ when it is shaded.

7. Makeup containing _____ may cause a foundation to turn ashy on dark skin.

8. Artificial eyelashes should be trimmed and _____ before they are applied.

CHAPTER 27

The Salon Business

Date _____

Rating _____

Text Pages 506–521

TOPIC 1—WHAT YOU SHOULD KNOW ABOUT THE SALON BUSINESS

1. As a salon owner, successful operation requires that you be both esthetician and owner at the same time.

   a. What are the three major building blocks that constitute the viability of a business?

   1. _____

   2. _____

   3. _____

   b. When getting started, what is your first order of business?

   _____

   c. Who should you select next? _____

2. Costs can be divided into fixed and variable costs.

   a. What's the difference?

   _____

   b. Give four examples of fixed costs.

   1. _____

   2. _____

   3. _____

   4. _____

c. Give five examples of variable costs.

1. _____

2. _____

3. _____

4. _____

5. _____

d. What happens when you get a handle on cost?

_____

_____

_____

_____

3. What is business forecasting?

_____

_____

_____

4. Name three considerations when selecting a location.

a. _____

b. _____

c. _____

5. Name eight considerations when negotiating a lease.

a. _____

b. _____

c. _____

d. _____

e. _____

f. _____

g. _____

h. _____

6. The layout of a salon is important to its efficient operation. Why is the reception area so important to the success of the salon?

_____

_____

7. Business problems are numerous, especially when you are a beginner in business.

   a. Name four common causes of business failure.

   1. _____

   2. _____

   3. _____

   4. _____

8. Good business administration demands keeping accurate records.

   a. Name two important reasons accurate records must be kept.

   1. _____

   2. _____

   b. Why is it important to keep accurate records of customer services?

   _____

Word Review

agreement	income tax	mortgage	proprietorship
budgeting	insurance coverage	overhead	regulations
competition	inventory	partnership	stockholder
contract	job description	personnel	supplies
corporation	labor laws	physical layout	trading area
efficiency	lease	projections	visible
full-service salon	local laws		

Date_____

Rating_____

Text Pages 521–525

TOPIC 2—TELEPHONE TECHNIQUES AND EFFICIENCY IN THE SALON

1. An important part of salon business is conducted over the telephone.

   a. Name the seven most useful purposes of the telephone in the salon.

   1. _____

   2. _____

   3. _____

   4. _____

   5. _____

6. _____

7. _____

b. Briefly describe the four basic rules for good telephone usage in the salon.

1. _____

2. _____

3. _____

4. _____

c. Name three attributes of a good telephone personality.

1. _____

2. _____

3. _____

2. A salon should be run in a safe and efficient manner.

a. In case of accident or serious illness of employees or clients, what should you do?

_____

b. Five important telephone numbers (representing important services) should be near the telephone for emergencies. Name these services.

1. _____

2. _____

3. _____

4. _____

5. _____

c. In addition to knowing the location of fire extinguishers, what should you know about them?

_____

d. In addition to knowing where exits are located, what should you know about them?

_____

e. In addition to knowing where your first aid kit is, what should you do?

_____

Word Review

| appointment | courtesy | first aid | tact |
| confirmation | fire extinguisher | judgment | telephone usage |

CHAPTER 28

Selling Products and Services

Date _____

Rating _____

Text Pages 527–531

TOPIC 1—WHAT SELLING IS

1. Selling is ethical and helping, and the best salespeople are sought out by their clients.

    a. Why?_____

    _____

    b. What is consultative selling?

    _____

    c. Name three qualities you must have to guide your clients.

    1. _____

    2. _____

    3. _____

2. Promotions are special activities that get you noticed.

    a. Name three short-term benefits of promotions.

    1. _____

    2. _____

    3. _____

    b. Name three long-term benefits of promotions.

    1. _____

    2. _____

    3. _____

    _____

3. For a gift-with-service or gift-with-product promotion, a client purchases a service or product at full price and receives a free gift, usually a professional product, with it. Name four ways this type of promotion is effective.

a. _____

b. _____

c. _____

d. _____

4. Why should you be careful of running too many sales?

_____

_____

5. Advertising and promotion can take a variety of forms.

a. What is your most powerful advertising and promotion vehicle?

_____

b. Name two approaches to promoting your business through your present clientele.

1. _____

2. _____

6. If businesses near yours attract the kinds of clients you want, you can combine your promotional efforts.

a. What is this called? _____

b. Give an example. _____

_____

_____

7. Public speaking can help you build your business.

a. What are your goals when you address groups?

_____

_____

b. Before contacting organizations to address, prepare a lively lecture and make sure you have_____ .

8. Public service can have a positive effect on your business.

a. What's an advantage of public service?

_____

b. Give two examples of public service.

1. _____

2. _____

Word Review

bargain	expert	long term	referral
consultative selling	gift-with product	opportunities	self-confidence
cooperative promotions	gift-with-service	perceived value	selling
cost-effective	helping	professionalism	visuals
enthusiasm	holidays	promotions	word-of-mouth
ethical	lean period	public speaking	

Rapid Review Test

Date_____

Rating_____

Insert the proper term in the space provided.

discounting	experience	promotion
everybody's	giving back	visuals

1. Selling is _____ business.

2. Without good _____ , your sales would stagnate or decline.

3. A promotion entices your clients to _____ a new product or service.

4. Generally speaking, you should avoid _____ products.

5. _____ can be slides, posters, or charts.

6. Your clients will think more highly of you if they know you are _____ to your community.

Date_____

Rating_____

Text Pages 531–535

TOPIC 2—ADVERTISING

1. What are the two points to keep in mind about advertising?

    a. _____

    b. _____

2. Name four things you must know to establish your business goals.

    a. _____

b. _____

c. _____

d. _____

3. Consistency means that your advertising is focused and has consistent elements. Give examples of elements that must be consistent.

   a. _____

   b. _____

   c. _____

   d. _____

   e. _____

4. While you want your advertising to be consistent, it also must be fresh.
   a. Name four ways to keep your advertising exciting.

   1. _____

   2. _____

   3. _____

   4. _____

5. What does K.I.S.S. stand for? _____

6. An ad campaign is better than an ad.
   a. What will a campaign bring to your advertising?

   1. _____

   2. _____

   3. _____

7. Your business will grow if you do what?

   _____

   _____

8. When your ad campaign has matured, you will notice a marked decline of how much in response to your ads? _____

9. Once your campaign has reached its decline, what can you do?

   _____

   _____

10. If your advertising isn't generating the response you want, what should you do?

   _____

11. Advertising can take a variety of forms.

    a. Give six examples of media for advertising.

    1. _____

    2. _____

    3. _____

    4. _____

    5. _____

    6. _____

    b. What's the best way to choose the right media for your ad?

    _____

    c. What is seen as the most selective and efficient form of advertising?

    _____

    d. Coupon packs or card decks are very cost-efficient, typically costing how much?

    _____

12. What can an advertising agency do?

    a. _____

    b. _____

    c. _____

    d. _____

13. Once a business is established, what is considered a normal advertising expenditure?

    _____

14. Why should you track your advertising results?

    _____

Word Review

advertising	cycle	investment	poll
agencies	decline	K.I.S.S.	radio
benefits	direct mail	logo	selective
campaigns	features	matured	slogans
card decks	flexible	media	taste
catchword	focus	newspapers	television
consistency	fresh	organization	tracking
coupons	image		

Rapid Review Test

Date_____

Rating_____

Insert the proper term in the space provided.

cycle   expensive   plan   twice

decline   five   selective   wisely

1. To make advertising pay off, you must _____ carefully.

2. Your reader has _____ seconds to figure out why an ad is of interest to him or her.

3. Advertising typically operates on a _____ .

4. The last phase of a campaign is its _____ .

5. Choosing the wrong media can be an _____ mistake.

6. Poll your clients at least _____ a year.

7. Being _____ is part of being focused.

8. If your advertising is not working, don't just think about spending more, think about spending more _____ .

Date_____

Rating_____

Text Pages 535–540

TOPIC 3—INTERPERSONAL COMMUNICATION SKILLS

1. Advertising and promotion bring people into the salon. What does everything thereafter depend on? _____

2. Effective selling means solving your clients' problems. What is this approach called?

   _____

3. Name the seven steps to simplified consultative selling.

   a. _____

   b. _____

   c. _____

   d. _____

e. _____

f. _____

g. _____

4. Your telephone conversations with your clients are often your opportunities for making good first impressions.

   a. Name the two basics of good phone communication.

      1. _____

      2. _____

   b. How can you cultivate your phone voice?

      _____

   c. What is the best way to respond to a phone inquiry?

      _____

5. What are the 11 steps to responding to price inquiries as a consultant?

   a. _____

   b. _____

   c. _____

   d. _____

   e. _____

   f. _____

   g. _____

   h. _____

   _____

   _____

   i. _____

   _____

   j. _____

   _____

   k. _____

6. Successful calling will result in a payoff for your business.

   a. Name four reasons to call your clients.

      1. _____

      2. _____

      3. _____

      4. _____

b. Name three ways calling pays off.

1. _____

2. _____

3. _____

c. Name the seven steps to successful calling.

1. _____

2. _____

3. _____

4. _____

5. _____

6. _____

7. _____

7. Professional-looking displays are essential to good selling. Name the eight points of a successful display.

a. _____

b. _____

c. _____

d. _____

e. _____

f. _____

g. _____

h. _____

Word Review

advice	gestures	professional image
analyze	guidance	psychology
attention	information	recommentions
benefits	interest	relationship
brief	listening	schedule
courteous	poll	shelf talkers
displays	positives	survey
experienced	professional	telephone
followup		

Rapid Review Test

Date_____

Rating_____

Place the correct word in spaces provided in the sentences below.

attention	choices	contact	limited
category	communication	impulse	relationship

1. Consultative selling relies on an ongoing _____ between client and esthetician.

2. On the phone, you should answer questions, but do not be _____ by them.

3. Your relationships with your clients are built on _____ and _____ .

4. Good lighting draws _____ to your display.

5. Clients like having _____ .

6. Products should be grouped by _____ , with the front labels clearly visible and lined up.

7. _____ -buy items, such as jewelry or small boutique items, should be located next to the cash register.

GENERAL REVIEW

COMPLETION TEST

Directions. Carefully read each statement. Insert the proper term in the space provided.

1. A powdered metallic substance used on the eyes of ancient Egyptians is called _____ .

2. Coloring matter used in early cosmetics were not synthetic but came from _____ sources such as trees, berries, herbs, and leaves.

3. The "Cupid's Bow" referred to a lip makeup style of the 19 _____ .

4. A salon that offers all services, from hair and skin care to manicuring, is called a full _____ salon.

5. The word "esthetics" or "aesthetics" was first used by _____ skin care specialists.

6. Personal hygiene concerns personal _____ .

7. The maintenance of healthy teeth and gums is called _____ hygiene.

8. Good posture helps the internal organs to function properly, improves appearance, and prevents _____ .

9. When walking or standing, weight should be on the _____ of the feet, not on the heels.

10. Personality analysis helps you improve yourself personally and _____ .

11. The most serious errors of good English are the use of slang, poor _____ , and vulgarisms.

12. A satisfied client is your best means of _____ .

13. Bacteriology is the science or study of _____ .

14. Germs and microbes are also called _____ .

15. Vegetable or animal organisms that thrive on living matter are called _____ .

16. Bacteria that thrive on dead matter are called _____ .

17. Natural _____ means you have a natural resistance to diseases.

191

18. Infectious _____ can be spread from one person to another.

19. A 37-40% solution of formaldehyde gas dissolved in water makes the solution called _____ .

20. Creams and other products used in the salon should be removed from containers with a _____ , not with the hands.

21. A _____ is the basic unit of all living things.

22. The reproduction of cells takes place by indirect _____ .

23. The stratum corneum is the _____ layer of the skin.

24. The stratum lucidum is the _____ layer of the skin.

25. The stratum germinativum is the _____ layer of the skin.

26. The stratum granulosum is the _____ layer of the skin.

27. One-half to two-thirds of the body's entire _____ supply is distributed to the skin.

28. Arrector pili muscles are attached to _____ follicles.

29. Sweat glands are found on the entire area of skin and are more numerous on the palms, soles, forehead, and in the _____ .

30. The natural lubricant of the skin is called _____ .

31. A skin specialist who treats diseases is called a _____ .

32. A chronic inflammatory disorder of the sebaceous (oil) glands, occurring especially during adolescence, is called _____ .

33. Miliaria ruba is commonly known as prickly _____ .

34. Bromidrosis is the term for foul smelling _____ .

35. "Hyperidrosis" refers to excessive _____ .

36. Bone, other than the _____ is the hardest structure of the body.

37. The _____ bone joins together all the cranial bones of the head.

38. The bony chest cage is called the _____ .

39. The largest bone of the upper arm is called the _____ .

40. Muscles attached to bones are usually referred to as _____ muscles.

41. The more movable attachment of a muscle is called the _____ of a muscle.

42. Striated muscular tissue, controlled by the will, are called _____ muscles.

43. Non-striated muscle tissue, smooth and involuntary, function without the control of the _____ .

44. The muscles of the head, face, neck, arms, and hands are of most concern to the esthetician. These are _____ muscles.

45. The cerebro-spinal or central nervous system consists of the _____ and spinal cord.

46. Thick-walled muscular and elastic tubes that transport blood from the heart to the capillaries are called _____ .

47. Blood circulation from the heart to the lungs is called _____ circulation.

48. The drainage system for body tissues is called the _____ system.

49. The _____ in the digestive secretions are responsible for the changes in food during digestion.

50. Matter may be changed in two ways, by physical or _____ means.

51. A compound used to lighten hair and as an antiseptic is hydrogen _____ .

52. In most cases _____ or filtered water is used in salon machines that require water.

53. The liquid known as the universal solvent is _____ .

54. Miscible substances are those that readily _____ with each other.

55. An antiperspirant checks _____ by its astringent action.

56. The esthetician should become familiar with common ingredients used in the manufacture of _____ .

57. The term _____ , as applied to food, means that the food has not been treated by chemical or _____ means.

58. Laws governing the manufacture of cosmetics are regulated by the Federal Food and _____ Administration.

59. Advertising of cosmetics is controlled by the Federal _____ Commission.

60. Studies reveal that poor _____ may be responsible for slow development and some skin problems in school children.

61. The most important carbohydrate used by the body is _____ , which is stored in the muscles and liver as glycogen.

62. One of the main sources of protein used in cosmetics is called _____ .

63. A calorie is a unit of _____ .

64. A well balanced diet provides the _____ needed to keep the skin healthy.

65. Severe vitamin C deficiency can cause scurvy, which produces ugly _____ .

66. Disease of the liver can cause the skin to have a _____ cast or color.

67. The endocrine glands produce _____ , which are sometimes added to cosmetics.

68. Tobacco contains _____ , which may affect blood vessels and slow the circulation.

69. Before examining a client's skin, the esthetician should _____ his or her hands.

70. During the analysis of the client's skin, the esthetician must determine the skin type, texture, and _____ of the skin.

71. A _____ skin is more prone to lining and wrinkling.

72. Infected ducts or pores that have become clogged with oil, dead cells, and dirt may cause _____ (comedones).

73. Accumulations of sebum underneath the unbroken surface of the skin may cause _____ (milia).

74. The oily area of the forehead, nose, and chin is called the T- _____ .

75. If a bar of soap has high alkalinity or a pH range of 10, it may be too irritating because the pH of the skin is approximately _____ .

76. Before giving facial treatments, the face must be thoroughly _____ .

77. Massage movements are usually directed toward the origin of _____ , to avoid damage to muscular tissue.

78. Friction and circular rubbing movements have a marked influence on circulation and _____ activity of the skin.

79. The main ingredient in an herbal mask that causes it to thicken or gel is called _____ .

80. A thin transparent fabric called _____ is used to keep mask ingredients from sliding off the face.

81. When an electric vaporizer is unavailable to steam the face, warm, moist _____ may be used.

82. After the application of a treatment cream, the client may be placed under the infra _____ lamp for a few minutes.

83. An alternative treatment for oil dry skin is the _____ mask or epidermabrasion treatment.

84. Waste products and _____ dioxide are carried away by the bloodstream, thus cleansing the skin of impurities.

85. Oxygen is essential to cell growth and is brought to the cells by the _____ .

86. Fulling is a form of _____ used mainly to massage the arms.

87. The motor nerve points affect the underlying _____ of the face and neck.

88. The main purpose of massage 2 is to aid in the deep _____ of products into the skin and to induce relaxation.

89. Galvanic current is a constant and _____ current rectified to a safe, low-voltage level.

90. A polarity changer alters the _____ of the current.

TRUE OR FALSE TEST—SUCCESSFUL SALON MANAGEMENT

Directions. Carefully read each statement, and check the box under the word you feel answers the question correctly.

	TRUE	FALSE
1. The esthetician should know something about salon management, whether or not he or she wants to own a salon.	☐	☐
2. A full-service salon is one that offers only one type of facial treatment.	☐	☐
3. A good salon location will have a population large enough to support the salon.	☐	☐
4. It is not necessary for a modern salon to attract the attention of people who walk or drive past the salon.	☐	☐
5. It generally draws more business when several salons are located in the same area.	☐	☐
6. It is necessary to locate a salon in an area made up of the type of clientele you hope to attract.	☐	☐
7. Today it is necessary, more than ever, to have written agreements.	☐	☐
8. In conducting business and employing help, it is necessary for the salon manager and owner to comply with local, state, and federal laws and regulations.	☐	☐
9. A client cannot bring a malpractice suit against a salon owner.	☐	☐
10. The reception area of a salon is not as important to clients as impressive machines.	☐	☐

11. A pleased client is the best form of advertising for a salon. ☐ ☐

12. The Yellow Pages of a telephone book is a poor place to advertise your salon. ☐ ☐

13. Anyone working in a salon should be a walking advertisement for its products and services. ☐ ☐

14. It is not necessary to have a salon budget if you take in more than monthly expenses. ☐ ☐

15. The largest expenses for most salons are in the form of salaries, rent, supplies, and advertising. ☐ ☐

16. Overhead is what must be paid before you can realize the profit needed to expand your business. ☐ ☐

17. The way appointments are booked can make the difference between the success or failure of a salon. ☐ ☐

18. In a salon, wise management of time is a major factor in gaining profits. ☐ ☐

19. Good business administration demands keeping accurate records. ☐ ☐

20. Service and inventory records should concern only the manager. ☐ ☐

21. The appointment book should show what is taking place in the salon at a given time. ☐ ☐

22. A salon may be owned and operated by individuals or in a partnership only. ☐ ☐

23. If you buy a salon from a friend, no written purchase or sale agreement is necessary. ☐ ☐

24. The telephone is the main line of communication between your salon and your clients. ☐ ☐

25. Any person who receives or places calls for your salon should be acquainted with and use all the rules of proper telephone courtesy. ☐ ☐

26. All salon personnel should be trained in the basics of first aid. ☐ ☐

27. The salon may be held responsible for a client who is injured on the premises; therefore, insurance is a must. ☐ ☐

28. All salons should have emergency telephone numbers posted where they can be seen. ☐ ☐

	TRUE	FALSE
29. All salon personnel should know where exits are located and how to handle serious emergencies should they occur.	☐	☐
30. One of the first rules for successful selling of products is to be familiar with their benefits.	☐	☐
31. A successful salesperson will recognize the needs of different types of people.	☐	☐
32. Selling power means being positive in a courteous and friendly manner.	☐	☐
33. It is better to sell the client what he or she needs rather than use pressure tactics to oversell.	☐	☐
34. Manufacturer's displays should be avoided because they tend to clutter the salon.	☐	☐
35. The esthetician should always suggest products for the client's home skin care regimen.	☐	☐
36. A client who has come to the salon for another service should not be asked if he or she would like a facial treatment.	☐	☐
37. The esthetician is never required to demonstrate his or her skills before being accepted for employment.	☐	☐
38. A resume or data sheet is just as important to a salon owner when hiring an esthetician as it is to another business owner hiring a secretary.	☐	☐
39. Schools are obligated to find jobs for their graduates.	☐	☐
40. Students should start looking for job opportunities before graduation.	☐	☐
41. All salons have the same systems; therefore, you will not be asked to adapt to new routines.	☐	☐
42. Good human relations refers to successful interpersonal relationships with family, socially, and on the job.	☐	☐
43. A beginner should never ask what a job pays until after he or she has been hired.	☐	☐
44. If you expect to be taken seriously at a job interview, you must look, speak, and act the part of the professional esthetician.	☐	☐
45. An esthetician should, when possible, become involved in services in the community that call attention to his or her work and place of business.	☐	☐

46. An esthetician, like a hairdresser, is expected to build a following of   ☐   ☐
loyal clients.

47. Once you have acquired a license to practice esthetics, you will not   ☐   ☐
be required to take more training on the job.

48. When on the phone, it is not professional to address clients by first name.   ☐   ☐

49. Trade papers, magazines, and newsletters are all sources of valu-   ☐   ☐
able information that help you keep abreast of developments in
your field.

50. The professional esthetician should join an organization that offers   ☐   ☐
educational seminars and conferences.

TEST I

Multiple Choice or Selection Test

Carefully read each statement. Underline the word or phrase which correctly completes the meaning of the statement.

1. Kohl was used by the ancient Egyptians as a/an

   a. hand cream   c. hair coloring

   b. eye makeup   d. lip makeup

2. The practice of cosmetology has its origin in

   a. the Renaissance period   c. the Roman era

   b. Greek civilization   d. ancient times

3. The earliest uses of cosmetics have been traced to the ancient

   a. Egyptians   c. Greeks

   b. Romans   d. Phoenicians

4. Face shaving was made popular by the

   a. Romans   c. Greeks

   b. Hebrews   d. Egyptians

5. Vermillion was used by ancient Greek women as a

   a. hair coloring   c. hair dressing

   b. skin lubricant   d. lip coloring

6. The Victorian Age was regarded as a period that was most

    a. austere and restrictive   c. colorful and joyous

    b. elaborate and extravagant   d. carefree and open

7. In the early postwar years, clothing fashions and hairstyles were strongly influenced by

    a. European designers   c. war phobia

    b. victory celebrations   d. military fashions

8. During the 1920s, fashions in clothing and hairstyles were largely influenced by

    a. industrial development   c. movie stars

    b. historical traditions   d. the Renaissance

9. Africans have been credited with the development of many medicines and grooming materials from substances in their

    a. tribal rituals   c. environment

    b. Renaissance   d. diet

10. In the 1970s, makeup for both day and evening wear became more

    a. drab   c. subdued

    b. colorful   d. disregarded

11. Estheticians specialize in the practice of

    a. manicuring   c. barber styling

    b. hairstyling   d. skin care

12. "Esthetics," a word describing the varied forms of beauty, originated in

    a. France   c. United States

    b. England   d. Italy

13. In some states, an esthetician must first be licensed as a

    a. manicurist   c. barber-stylist

    b. cosmetologist   d. podiatrist

14. A restorative art specialist is someone who works with

    a. television performers   c. licensed morticians

    b. film actors   d. theater groups

15. The licensing of estheticians is usually handled by the

    a. state board   c. teaching supervisor

    b. school director   d. accrediting commission

16. A physician who specializes in the practice of that branch of medical science that deals with skin disorders is a

    a. physiologist   c. psychologist

    b. dermatologist   d. psychiatrist

17. A career in the field of merchandising requires an ability to

    a. produce   c. teach

    b. communicate   d. remove hair

18. An individual employed by a manufacturer to study, develop, and test new products is called a/an

    a. research specialist   c. esthetician specialist

    b. dermatologist   d. makeup specialist

19. An esthetician employed as a research specialist or assistant must have a background in

    a. makeup   c. medicine

    b. hairstyling   d. chemistry

20. Individuals who give facials and apply personalized makeup in licensed salons are called

    a. surgeons   c. therapists

    b. dermatologists   d. estheticians

21. Hygiene is the branch of applied science that deals with

    a. chemistry   c. algebra

    b. healthful living   d. biology

22. Personal hygiene is the practice of preserving the health of

    a. the community   c. individuals

    b. government officials   d. groups

23. "Public hygiene" or "sanitation" refers to the practice of promoting the health of the

    a. community   c. patron

    b. individual   d. cosmetologist

24. A physical examination is required of estheticians to assure that they are

    a. of the proper age

    c. physically capable

    b. properly vaccinated

    d. free from contagious disease

25. Good grooming is part of

    a. personal hygiene

    c. public safety

    b. public sanitation

    d. government requirements

26. Healthy teeth can be maintained by

    a. use of mouthwash

    c. physical exercise

    b. regular dental care

    d. strict dieting

27. Bad breath is usually eliminated by the use of a/an

    a. deodorant

    c. sanitized toothbrush

    b. mouthwash

    d. astringent

28. Exercise helps to

    a. circulate the blood

    c. keep skin clean

    b. eliminate bad breath

    d. prevent malnutrition

29. Public hygiene is valuable to everyone because it

    a. preserves the health of the individual

    c. preserves the health of the community

    b. helps maintain the quality of esthetic services

    d. aids in the training of estheticians

30. The digestive system can be aided in functioning properly by

    a. improper nutrition

    c. irregular habits

    b. a balanced diet

    d. eating high-calorie foods

31. The branch of science that deals with healthful living is

    a. hygiene

    c. cosmetology

    b. dermatology

    d. esthetics

32. A person should not be permitted to attend a school of beauty culture if he or she is suffering from a/an

    a. gout disorder

    c. infectious disease

    b. arthritic disorder

    d. broken bone

33. A healthy attitude can be cultivated by

    a. legislative action

    b. license laws

    c. self-control

    d. temper tantrums

34. Angry thoughts often may cause the heart action to

    a. stop

    b. slow up

    c. retrogress

    d. increase

35. Poor eating habits and lack of nutrition may result in a

    a. ruddy complexion

    b. cheerful disposition

    c. healthful appearance

    d. dull complexion

36. Correct posture is important to the esthetician because it helps to

    a. prevent acne

    b. maintain clear skin

    c. improve the complexion

    d. prevent fatigue

37. When walking or standing, flexed knees

    a. help correct flat feet

    b. prevent ingrown toenails

    c. prevent bow legs

    d. act as shock absorbers

38. To avoid back strain when sitting in a chair

    a. sit well back

    b. sit forward

    c. lean against the sides

    d. lean on the arms

39. The common name of the condition known as "lordosis" is

    a. slumped posture

    b. swayback

    c. dropped shoulders

    d. flat feet

40. The weight of the body should be carried on the

    a. toes of the feet

    b. heels of the feet

    c. ankles

    d. balls of the feet

41. To maintain good posture, the esthetician should wear

    a. well fitted shoes

    b. high-heel shoes

    c. slippers

    d. pointed-toe shoes

42. Malformed feet and aching backs often are the result of

    a. regular foot exercises

    b. sitting stance

    c. poorly fitted shoes

    d. strong arches

43. One factor that helps the internal organs function properly is

    a. good posture

    b. lordosis posture

    c. heavy muscles

    d. scoliosis

44. An example of self-discipline is

    a. speaking your mind

    b. greed

    c. anger

    d. restraint

45. The root of politeness is

    a. self-indulgence

    b. fear

    c. thoughtfulness of others

    d. speaking carefully

46. Since words alone do not project your personality, the esthetician should develop a

    a. loud voice

    b. pleasant voice

    c. high-pitched voice

    d. shrill voice

47. To ensure success, treat each client as a/an

    a. young woman

    b. very important person

    c. complainer

    d. inferior

48. A very important attribute of a pleasing personality is a good

    a. financial standing

    b. list of stories

    c. political background

    d. sense of humor

49. The use of good speech is vital to the art of

    a. literature

    b. conversation

    c. fashion

    d. grooming

50. Good topics for salon conversation are

    a. political

    b. controversial

    c. noncontroversial

    d. debatable

51. The esthetician should try to fit a conversation to the client's

    a. service

    b. mood

    c. religion

    d. politics

52. Determining right and wrong conduct in relationships with others is called

    a. personality

    b. ethics

    c. serenity

    d. politics

53. Extravagant claims and unfilled promises by an esthetician are examples of

    a. good ethics

    b. great ability

    c. poor ethics

    d. a good personality

54. Clients should be addressed by their

    a. nicknames

    b. names

    c. numbers

    d. personalities

55. It is often a good idea for the esthetician to be a good

    a. gossiper

    b. listener

    c. babbler

    d. complainer

56. A client will show loyalty and respect to an esthetician who is

    a. depressed

    b. dependable

    c. loud

    d. overly familiar

57. The study and philosophy of human conduct is referred to as

    a. circumstantial evidence

    b. professional ethics

    c. security study

    d. cooperative studies

58. A set of high moral principles and values is a prerequisite for building

    a. arrogance

    b. esthetics

    c. techniques

    d. confidence

59. Success in business is promoted by business sense and

    a. familiarity with clients

    b. sales ability

    c. depressed nature

    d. overpricing clients

60. It is necessary to handle clients' complaints

    a. roughly   c. judiciously

    b. grudgingly   d. slowly

61. The first requirement of success is your ability to

    a. overprice clients   c. talk continuously

    b. fool clients   d. make people like you

TEST II

Multiple Choice or Selection Test

Carefully read each statement. Underline the word or phrase which correctly completes the meaning of the statement.

1. The study of micro-organisms is known as

    a. genetics   c. chemistry

    b. bacteriology   d. biology

2. The French bacteriologist known for his work with microbes was

    a. Albert Einstein   c. Louis Pasteur

    b. Benjamin Franklin   d. Jonas Salk

3. A more common name for bacteria is

    a. diseases   c. cold sores

    b. germs   d. insects

4. Harmless bacteria are called

    a. contagious   c. homogenized

    b. pathogenic   d. nonpathogenic

5. The majority of all bacteria is

    a. harmless   c. visible to the naked eye

    b. deadly   d. animal

6. Pathogenic bacteria are

    a. harmless   c. antiseptic

    b. harmful   d. dry

7. The shape of cocci bacteria is

   a. round

   b. rodlike

                  c. corkscrewlike

                  d. curved

8. Bacilli have a

   a. round shape

   b. corkscrew shape

                  c. rod shape

                  d. curved shape

9. Spirilla bacteria have a

   a. square shape

   b. round shape

                  c. rod shape

                  d. corkscrew shape

10. During the active stage, bacteria

   a. die

   b. grow

                  c. remain the same

                  d. are in spore form

11. Bacteria grow best in places that are

   a. bright and sunny

   b. cool and light

                  c. damp and dirty

                  d. clean and dry

12. An example of a spore-forming bacteria is

   a. cilia

   b. flagella

                  c. pus

                  d. tetanus

13. An example of a local infection is

   a. blood poisoning

   b. a boil

                  c. a cold

                  d. a broken arm

14. A contagious disease is

   a. caused by nonpathogenic bacteria

   b. a poison

                  c. nontransferable

                  d. spread from one person to another

15. Contagious bacteria may enter the body through skin that is

   a. oily

   b. normal

                  c. broken

                  d. dry

16. A common source of infection is

    a. old implements

    b. sterilized implements

    c. dirty implements

    d. new implements

17. Scabies is caused by a bacteria whose origin is

    a. animal

    b. vegetable

    c. mineral

    d. chemical

18. The ability of the body to resist and destroy bacteria is known as

    a. infection

    b. contagion

    c. immunity

    d. susceptibility

19. Immunity that is inherited is referred to as being

    a. acquired

    b. natural

    c. obtained

    d. relinquished

20. Vaccination is effective against

    a. measles

    b. colds

    c. scabies

    d. ringworm

21. Penicillin is a/an

    a. disease

    b. antibiotic

    c. parasite

    d. immunity

22. Antibodies may be produced by

    a. molds

    b. insects

    c. one's own body

    d. exercise

23. It is important that estheticians study bacteriology to assist them in their efforts to prevent the

    a. loss of income

    b. spread of disease

    c. loss of skills

    d. loss of clients

24. The active (growing) stage in the bacterial life cycle is called the

    a. vegetative stage

    b. pathogenic stage

    c. spore-forming stage

    d. cocci stage

25. The inactive (resting) stage in the bacterial life cycle is called the

    a. bacillus stage   c. treponema stage

    b. vegetative stage   d. spore-forming stage

26. A person who is already immune to a disease, but may infect others, is known as a/an

    a. immunizer   c. conditioner

    b. carrier   d. micro-organism

27. A substance that hinders the growth of or destroys another type of organism is a/an

    a. antibiotic   c. parasite

    b. virus   d. disintegrator

28. Bacteria can be destroyed by

    a. antiseptics   c. deodorants

    b. boric acid   d. disinfectants

29. One of the body's most important defenses against disease is a/an

    a. strong skeleton   c. healthy skin

    b. enlarged heart   d. disinfectants

30. The body defends itself from harmful bacteria by producing

    a. inflammation   c. pathogenic germs

    b. vaccines   d. spirillum

31. Sterilization is the process of

    a. helping bacteria to grow   c. destroying all bacteria

    b. destroying only nonpathogenic bacteria   d. destroying only harmful bacteria

32. Using boiling water to sterilize is the method called

    a. moist heat   c. baking

    b. fumigation   d. chemical

33. When removing cream products from a container, the esthetician should use

    a. the fingers   c. the hand

    b. a spatula   d. ends of towels

34. A dry or cabinet sanitizer contains an active

  a. styptic

  b. sanitized towel

  c. deodorant

  d. fumigant

35. To be effective, a wet sanitizer should contain

  a. boiling water

  b. 2% formalin

  c. a disinfectant

  d. deodorizer

36. Sanitize sharp metallic instruments with

  a. 70% alcohol

  b. 20% alcohol

  c. 50% alcohol

  d. 30% alcohol

37. Formaldehyde is an active gas found in

  a. oxygen

  b. chlorine

  c. sulphur

  d. formalin

38. Quaternary ammonium compounds are used as

  a. deodorants

  b. antiseptics

  c. disinfectants

  d. antibiotics

39. Electrodes may be sanitized with

  a. boiling water

  b. 70% alcohol

  c. sulphur

  d. boric acid

40. To disinfect properly, quaternary ammonium compounds require a

  a. mixture of boric acid

  b. mixture of formalin

  c. long contact time

  d. short contact time

41. The use of quaternary ammonium compounds is an example of disinfecting by

  a. steam

  b. chemicals

  c. boiling water

  d. ultraviolet rays

42. To be an effective sanitizer, the strength of alcohol should be

  a. 50%

  b. 70%

  c. 45%

  d. 60%

43. A fumigant often is used to keep sanitized implements in a

    a. dry condition   c. clean condition

    b. wet condition   d. sanitary condition

44. The regulation governing the use of towels stipulates that they

    a. be neatly folded after each use c. are a regulation size

    b. be laundered after each use   d. always look clean

45. Most bacteria are destroyed by

    a. antiseptics   c. ice water

    b. soap suds   d. ultraviolet rays

46. A chemical agent having the power to destroy bacteria is a/an

    a. boric acid   c. endocrine

    b. epidermal   d. germicide

47. A cell is the basic unit of all

    a. chemicals   c. dead matter

    b. living matter   d. cosmetics

48. A cell is a minute portion of living substance containing

    a. minerals   c. tissues

    b. protoplasm   d. gases

49. The part of a cell that is vitally important to reproduction is called the

    a. membrane   c. nucleus

    b. protoplasm   d. gland

50. The portion of a cell containing food for growth and repair is called the

    a. cytoplasm   c. nucleus

    b. protoplasm   d. gland

51. The nucleus is surrounded by the

    a. centrosome   c. nuclear membrane

    b. cell   d. cytoplasm

52. The complex process whereby cells are nourished is called

    a. cytoplasm

    c. metabolism

    b. protoplasm

    d. mitosis

53. Anabolism and catabolism are two phases of

    a. metabolism

    c. mitosis

    b. reproduction

    d. amitosis

54. Human cells reproduce by dividing in

    a. fourths

    c. halves

    b. fifths

    d. thirds

55. The reproduction of a human cell is a complex process called

    a. direct division

    c. metabolism

    b. indirect division

    d. cellular repair

56. Body tissue consists of a group of similar

    a. minerals

    c. bacteria

    b. cells

    d. gases

57. A body system is a group of

    a. glands

    c. chemicals

    b. organs

    d. gases

58. The system composed of the bones of the body is called the

    a. circulatory system

    c. muscular system

    b. digestive system

    d. skeletal system

59. The human body contains the following number of important systems:

    a. 12

    c. 9

    b. 2

    d. 10

60. The basic units of all living things are the

    a. organs

    c. membranes

    b. tissues

    d. cells

61. The building up of cellular tissues is called

    a. cannibalism   c. anabolism

    b. catabolism   d. pigmentation

62. The breaking down of cellular tissues is called

    a. physiology   c. nutrition

    b. catabolism   d. anabolism

63. Tissues that serve to support, protect, and bind together other tissues of the body are

    a. connective tissues   c. nerve tissues

    b. muscular tissues   d. epithelial tissues

64. Tissues that carry food, waste products, and hormones to and from various parts of the body are

    a. epithelial tissues   c. connective tissues

    b. nerve tissues   d. liquid tissues

65. A type of tissue that serves as a protective covering on body surfaces is

    a. liquid tissue   c. epithelial tissue

    b. muscular tissue   d. nerve tissue

66. A structure containing two or more different tissues combined to perform a specific function is a/an

    a. system   c. structure

    b. organ   d. section

67. Groups or organs that cooperate for the welfare of the entire body are called

    a. sections   c. tissues

    b. systems   d. structures

68. The system that controls and coordinates the functions of all other systems is the

    a. endocrine system   c. excretory system

    b. circulatory system   d. nervous system

69. The system that affects the growth, reproduction, and health of the body is the

    a. endocrine system   c. excretory system

    b. respiratory system   d. muscular system

70. The system that supplies the body with oxygen and removes carbon dioxide is the

    a. respiratory system

    b. circulatory system

    c. nervous system

    d. reproductive system

71. The system that purifies the body by the elimination of waste products is the

    a. digestive system

    b. excretory system

    c. endocrine system

    d. respiratory system

72. Healthy skin is

    a. inflexible

    b. dry and scaly

    c. tight

    d. flexible

73. Healthy skin is

    a. slightly moist

    b. bluish in color

    c. pale in color

    d. scaly

74. The thickest skin on the human body can be found on the

    a. eyelids

    b. arms

    c. soles of the feet

    d. forehead

75. The outermost layer of the skin is called the

    a. dermis

    b. epidermis

    c. subcutaneous tissue

    d. connective tissue

76. The epidermis of the skin is made of a substance called

    a. dermis

    b. subcutaneous tissue

    c. connective tissue

    d. keratin

77. Keratin consists of

    a. protein

    b. bone

    c. muscle

    d. nerves

78. An example of hard keratin is the

    a. nail

    b. eyelid

    c. fingertip

    d. elbow

79. The epidermis contains

    a. four layers

    b. six layers

    c. five layers

    d. three layers

80. The layer of epidermis constantly shedding and replacing itself is known as the

    a. clear layer

    b. horny layer

    c. inner layer

    d. granular layer

81. Other names for the dermis are cutis, derma, corium, and

    a. epidermis

    b. lucidum skin

    c. true skin

    d. granulosum

82. The skin is nourished by

    a. blood and lymph

    b. insoluble chemicals

    c. water

    d. gases

83. The body is provided with a sense of touch by the layer of skin known as the

    a. clear layer

    b. papillary layer

    c. stratum germinativum

    d. horny layer

84. Melanin is a

    a. blood vessel

    b. color pigment

    c. chemical

    d. layer of the skin

85. The main function of sebum is to prevent the skin from

    a. losing moisture

    b. producing acne

    c. losing color

    d. melanin loss

86. The color of the skin is determined primarily by its

    a. oxygen content

    b. sebaceous glands

    c. sweat glands

    d. melanin

87. Sweat glands help to regulate

    a. body weight

    b. skin color

    c. body temperature

    d. body height

88. Another name of the oil glands of the skin is

    a. sebaceous glands

    b. pituitary glands

    c. thyroid glands

    d. thymus glands

89. Adipose tissue gives the skin and body

    a. elasticity

    b. color

    c. contour

    d. a sense of touch

90. An example of an appendage of the skin is

    a. blood vessels

    b. red corpuscles

    c. white corpuscles

    d. fingernails

91. The largest organ of the body is the

    a. skeleton

    b. skin

    c. heart

    d. liver

92. The skin is lubricated by secretions from the

    a. thyroid gland

    b. sweat glands

    c. sebaceous glands

    d. adrenal glands

93. The nail is an appendage of the

    a. skeleton

    b. sebaceous gland

    c. skin

    d. sweat gland

94. Most skin problems first are visible on the

    a. dermis

    b. sweat glands

    c. adrenals

    d. epidermis

95. The skin layer that gives skin strength, form, and flexibility is the

    a. epidermis

    b. lucidum

    c. corneum

    d. dermis

96. Blood vessels, oil glands, and sweat glands are contained within the

    a. dermis

    b. epidermis

    c. stratum corneum

    d. stratum lucidum

97. Nerves that react to heat, cold, touch, pressure, and pain are

    a. motor nerves

    b. sensory nerves

    c. secretory nerves

    d. sympathetic nerves

98. Hardened, darkened sebum in blocked follicles form

    a. milia

    b. blackheads

    c. whiteheads

    d. capillaries

99. The skin protects the body from injury and

    a. bacterial invasion

    b. sudoriferous secretions

    c. sebaceous secretions

    d. melanin invasion

100. Extreme stimulation of a sensory nerve ending produces

    a. pain

    b. relaxation

    c. lubrication

    d. sweat

TEST III

Multiple Choice or Selection Test

Carefully read each statement. Underline the word or phrase which correctly completes the meaning of the statement

1. The branch of medical science that deals with the skin, its diseases, and its treatment is called

    a. pathology

    b. dermatology

    c. podiatry

    d. psychiatry

2. An esthetician must be able to recognize serious skin diseases and refer clients to a

    a. dermatologist

    b. cosmetologist

    c. hospital

    d. psychologist

3. Pathology is the study of

    a. diseases

    b. skin

    c. cuticles

    d. blood

4. Etiology is the study of the

   a. causes of diseases

   b. effects of diseases

   c. treatment of diseases

   d. prognosis of diseases

5. Itching is an example of a/an

   a. subjective symptom

   b. objective symptom

   c. blister

   d. scab

6. A small discolored spot on the skin, such as a freckle, is a

   a. macule

   b. bulla

   c. pustule

   d. tumor

7. A papule is a

   a. secondary skin lesion

   b. primary skin lesion

   c. scaly skin lesion

   d. crusty skin lesion

8. A blister, or bulla, contains

   a. pus

   b. no fluid

   c. watery fluid

   d. epidermal flakes

9. Poison ivy is a contagious disease producing

   a. papules

   b. tubercles

   c. vesicles

   d. tumors

10. An insect bite or a case of hives is an example of a lesion called a

    a. macule

    b. scar

    c. wheel

    d. bulla

11. Secondary lesions are those that develop in the skin during which stage of disease?

    a. keratinizing

    b. early

    c. primary

    d. later

12. An example of flaky epidermal tissue is

    a. pus

    b. dandruff

    c. ulcers

    d. papules

13. A crack in the skin is known as a/an

    a. ulcer   c. scar

    b. tumor   d. fissure

14. Skin infections are characterized by objective lesions that are

    a. always contagious   c. invisible

    b. communicable   d. visible

15. Infectious skin diseases are caused by

    a. poor eating habits   c. pathogenic germs

    b. congenital germs   d. nonpathogenic germs

16. In describing a disease, the term "infectious" is often interchanged with the term

    a. occupational   c. parasitic

    b. communicable   d. seasonal

17. Oversensitivity to normally harmless substances or objects is called a/an

    a. allergy   c. milia

    b. comedone   d. disease

18. The technical name for "blackhead" is

    a. whitehead   c. dry skin

    b. comedone   d. acne

19. The activity of the sebaceous glands is usually stimulated during

    a. childhood   c. middle age

    b. adolescence   d. infancy

20. The technical name for "whitehead" is

    a. milia   c. comedone

    b. blackhead   d. acne

21. Simple acne is often referred to as "acne vulgaris" or

    a. acne seborrhea   c. acne simplex

    b. acne rosacea   d. acne furuncle

22. Acne rosacea is associated with excessive

    a. cleansing   c. dryness

    b. scaling   d. oiliness

23. A sebaceous cyst or subcutaneous tumor is technically called a/an

    a. asteatosis   c. furuncle

    b. rosacea   d. steatoma

24. A ruptured follicle deep within the dermis is often the cause of

    a. a cyst   c. seborrhea

    b. asteatosis   d. macule

25. The three types of acne scars are referred to as acne pit, raised scars, and

    a. icepick scars   c. rough pits

    b. scaly pits   d. dry scars

26. If it is necessary for the esthetician to prick the skin, it is recommended that he or she use a/an

    a. razor blade   c. lancet

    b. spatula   d. extractor

27. If the esthetician doubts that a pimple is ready for cleaning, it is best to

    a. clean it quickly   c. apply strong pressure

    b. leave it alone   d. clean it twice

28. "Bromidrosis" refers to

    a. lack of perspiration   c. clear perspiration

    b. excessive perspiration   d. foul-smelling perspiration

29. The technical term for skin inflammation is

    a. canities   c. dermatitis

    b. alopecia   d. anitrosis

30. The technical name for liver spots on the skin is

    a. leucoderma   c. chloasma

    b. naevus   d. albinism

31. Abnormal white patches on the skin are called

    a. leucoderma   c. naevus

    b. albinism   d. chloasma

32. A skin wart is known as a

    a. stain   c. naevus

    b. vitiligo   d. verruca

33. "Keratoma" is a technical term for a

    a. callous   c. stain

    b. wart   d. tan

34. Broken capillaries in skin appear as

    a. light patches   c. fine lines

    b. liver spots   d. deep frowns

35. As skin ages, lines appear around the eyes. These lines are commonly called

    a. warts   c. skin tags

    b. moles   d. crow's feet

36. Allergic dermatitis is another name for

    a. eczema   c. tumors

    b. venereal disease   d. melanomas

37. An uneven, jagged tear in the skin is called a/an

    a. abrasion   c. laceration

    b. scar   d. cyst

38. The narrow opening or furrow in the skin is known as a

    a. wart   c. boil

    b. fissure   d. puncture

39. A growth that extends from the skin is known as a/an

    a. puncture   c. fissure

    b. polyp   d. incision

40. The recognition of a disease from its symptoms is called the

    a. objective
    c. diagnosis

    b. prognosis
    d. subjective

41. The foretelling of the probable course of a disease is called the

    a. erythema
    c. symptom

    b. acanthosis
    d. prognosis

42. A structural tissue change caused by injury or disease is a

    a. diagnosis
    c. prognosis

    b. lesion
    d. follicle

43. A chronic inflammatory disorder of the skin is called

    a. acne
    c. steatoma

    b. seborrhea
    d. asteatosis

44. An open sore on the surface of the skin is called a/an

    a. nodule
    c. polyp

    b. ulcer
    d. cyst

45. A sensitivity that develops to a normally harmless substance is a/an

    a. steatoma
    c. hypertrophy

    b. allergy
    d. sedative

46. A round, thickened patch of epidermis, caused by friction, is called a

    a. leucoderma
    c. keratoma

    b. lentigines
    d. chloasma

TEST IV

Multiple Choice or Selection Test

Carefully read each statement. Underline the word or phrase which correctly completes the meaning of the statement.

1. One important function of the skeletal system is to

    a. give strength and shape to the body
    c. carry blood

    b. carry nerve impulses
    d. support ligaments

2. The skeletal system is comprised of

   a. muscles

   b. bones

   c. nerves

   d. tendons

3. The skull is divided into

   a. four parts

   b. three parts

   c. six parts

   d. two parts

4. The parietal bones form the top and sides of the

   a. neck

   b. jaw

   c. cranium

   d. face

5. The frontal bone forms the

   a. forehead

   b. jaw

   c. cheek

   d. nose

6. The ethmoid bones are located

   a. at the lower neck

   b. behind the ears

   c. between the eye sockets

   d. below the ear

7. Maxillae bones form the

   a. eye socket

   b. forehead

   c. upper jaw

   d. lower jaw

8. The bridge of the nose is formed by

   a. zygomatic bones

   b. maxillae bones

   c. nasal bones

   d. lacrimal bone

9. The cheeks are formed by the

   a. zygomatic bones

   b. maxillae bones

   c. nasal bones

   d. lacrimal bone

10. The upper part of the spinal column is formed by the cervical vertebrae, located in the

   a. chest region

   b. neck region

   c. skull region

   d. lower back region

11. The chest, an elastic bony cage, is also known as the

    a. ulna   c. thorax

    b. radius   d. humerus

12. The largest bone in the upper arm is called the

    a. humerus   c. wrist

    b. ulna   d. tibia

13. The study of muscles, their functions and their diseases, is known as

    a. physiology   c. biology

    b. bacteriology   d. myology

14. How many kinds of muscular tissue are there?

    a. two   c. three

    b. five   d. six

15. Muscles that are controlled by the will are called

    a. voluntary   c. involuntary

    b. nonstriated   d. cardiac

16. Muscles that are not controlled by will are called

    a. voluntary   c. skeletal

    b. striated   d. nonstriated

17. The heart is composed of

    a. striated muscle   c. cardiac muscle

    b. striped muscle   d. voluntary muscle

18. The muscle that covers the tip of the skull is called the

    a. orbicularis   c. procerus

    b. epicranius   d. oculi

19. The muscle that surrounds the eye socket and closes the eye is called the

    a. procerus   c. epicranius

    b. orbicularis oculi   d. frontalis

20. The muscle called "quadratus labii superioris" raises the

    a. ear   c. upper lip

    b. eye   d. lower lip

21. The quadratus labii inferioris muscle depresses the

    a. lower lip   c. eyebrows

    b. upper lip   d. eyelids

22. The muscle that draws the eyebrows down and in is the

    a. procerus   c. occipitalis

    b. epicranius   d. corrugator

23. The muscle that covers the top of the nose is the

    a. procerus   c. epicranius

    b. trapezius   d. maxillae

24. The sterno-cleido-mastoid muscle flexes the

    a. head   c. mouth

    b. eyes   d. nostrils

25. The mentalis muscle is located in the

    a. eye socket   c. chin

    b. ear   d. finger

26. The muscles that attach the arm to the body are the latissimus dorsi and the

    a. biceps   c. triceps

    b. trapezius   d. extensors

27. The pectoralis muscles, which assist in swinging movements of the arm, cover the

    a. elbows   c. back of the chest

    b. wrists   d. front of the chest

28. The principal muscles on the front of the upper arms are called the

    a. biceps   c. extensors

    b. trapezius   d. flexors

29. The branch of medicine that deals with the nervous system is called

    a. anatomy

    b. physiology

    c. chemistry

    d. neurology

30. The principal parts of the nervous system are the brain and the spinal cord and their

    a. blood vessels

    b. nerves

    c. glands

    d. organs

31. The cerebro-spinal system is also known as the

    a. sympathetic nervous system

    b. glandular nervous system

    c. peripheral nervous system

    d. central nervous system

32. The sensory and motor nerves are part of the

    a. central system

    b. voluntary system

    c. peripheral system

    d. glandular system

33. The cerebro-spinal nervous system controls the

    a. involuntary muscles

    b. voluntary muscles

    c. heart muscles

    d. digestive muscles

34. The central nervous system is composed of the brain and the

    a. sensory nerves

    b. muscles

    c. spinal cord

    d. heart

35. Afferent nerves also are called

    a. sensory nerves

    b. efferent nerves

    c. motor nerves

    d. nerve reflexes

36. Twelve pairs of cranial nerves originate in the brain and reach the

    a. stomach and hips

    b. legs and feet

    c. arms and hands

    d. head, face, and neck

37. Thirty-one pairs of nerves extend upward and downward from the

    a. brain

    b. head

    c. spinal cord

    d. face

38. The trifacial nerve is the chief sensory nerve of the

    a. hand   c. chest

    b. face   d. arm

39. The skin of the forehead, scalp, eyebrows, and upper eyelids are affected by the

    a. infra-trochlear   c. supra-orbital nerve

    b. nasal nerve   d. mental nerve

40. The skin between the eyes and the upper sides of the nose is affected by the

    a. supra-orbital nerve   c. supra-trochlear nerve

    b. zygomatic nerve   d. infra-trochlear nerve

41. The muscles of the upper part of the cheek are affected by the

    a. zygomatic nerve   c. mental nerve

    b. trifacial nerve   d. cervical nerve

42. The seventh cranial nerve is the chief motor nerve of the

    a. arm   c. hand

    b. face   d. chest

43. The temporal nerve affects the muscles of the eyelid, forehead, temple, and

    a. nose   c. upper lip

    b. eyebrow   d. lower lip

44. The blood vascular system consists of arteries, veins, capillaries, and

    a. lymph nodes   c. duct glands

    b. the heart   d. lacteals

45. The blood vascular system is also known as the

    a. glandular system   c. skeletal system

    b. circulatory system   d. muscular system

46. The heart has upper, thin-walled chambers called

    a. atria   c. ventricles

    b. valves   d. capillaries

47. Blood is prevented from flowing backward through the heart by

    a. valves

    b. vessels

    c. capillaries

    d. duct glands

48. The lower, thick-walled chambers of the heart are called

    a. atria

    b. valves

    c. ventricles

    d. capillaries

49. The blood cells that carry oxygen to the body are called

    a. platelets

    b. hemoglobin

    c. white corpuscles

    d. red corpuscles

50. The blood cells that fight bacteria are called

    a. platelets

    b. hemoglobin

    c. white corpuscles

    d. red corpuscles

51. The common carotid arteries are located at the sides of the

    a. neck

    b. face

    c. head

    d. nose

52. The bones of the body are united together by

    a. joints

    b. muscles

    c. nerves

    d. mandibles

53. The skeleton of the face consists of

    a. 8 bones

    b. 14 bones

    c. 2 bones

    d. 6 bones

54. The bone that forms the lower back part of the cranium is the

    a. occipital

    b. parietal

    c. temporal

    d. ethmoid

55. The bone that joins all the bones of the cranium is the

    a. mandible

    b. parietal

    c. spheroid

    d. temporal

56. The hyoid bone is often referred to as the

    a. spinal column

    b. jawbone

    c. spongy bone

    d. Adam's apple

57. Muscles are composed of

    a. contractile fibrous tissue

    b. masses of nerve cells

    c. firmly bound fibrous tissue

    d. pericardium membrane

58. The esthetician is primarily concerned with the

    a. voluntary muscles

    b. smooth muscles

    c. nonstriated muscles

    d. involuntary muscles

59. The involuntary muscles are serviced by the

    a. cerebro-spinal nervous system

    b. sympathetic nervous system

    c. central nervous system

    d. peripheral nervous system

60. Muscles contract and expand as a result of nerve

    a. relaxation

    b. stimulation

    c. fatigue

    d. growth

61. The main source of the supply of blood to head, face, and neck is the

    a. submental artery

    b. carotid artery

    c. inferior artery

    d. angular artery

62. The blood returns to the heart from the head and face by means of the

    a. auricular vein

    b. carotid arteries

    c. occipital vein

    d. inferior arteries

63. The liver, kidneys, skin, intestines, and lungs are part of the

    a. digestive system

    b. digestion

    c. excretory system

    d. conversion

64. The process of converting food into a form that can be assimilated by the body is called

    a. respiration

    b. digestion

    c. metabolism

    d. conversion

65. Organic chemistry is the study of all substances containing

    a. carbon

    b. water

    c. air

    d. lead

66. Matter is defined as anything that

    a. contains color

    b. occupies space

    c. floats on water

    d. has a gaseous form

67. The basic unit of matter is the

    a. element

    b. electron

    c. base

    d. proton

68. The smallest part of an element is the

    a. electron

    b. proton

    c. base

    d. atom

69. A substance formed by uniting two elements chemically is known as a/an

    a. atom

    b. molecule

    c. compound

    d. mixture

70. A combination of substances that are held together by physical rather than chemical bonds is called a

    a. mixture

    b. compound

    c. solvent

    d. synthesis

71. A preparation made by dissolving a solid, liquid, or gaseous substance is called a/an

    a. solute

    b. solution

    c. element

    d. ointment

72. The substance dissolved in the making of a solution is called a/an

    a. solute

    b. compound

    c. element

    d. ointment

73. The liquid used to dissolve a solute is called a/an

    a. element

    b. atom

    c. solvent

    d. compound

74. An example of a universal solvent is

    a. oxygen   c. water

    b. oil   d. gas

75. Solvents that readily mix are considered to be

    a. immiscible   c. incompatible

    b. miscible   d. volatile

76. A temporary mixture of insoluble powders in a liquid is called a/an

    a. compound   c. emulsion

    b. element   d. suspension

77. A more permanent mixture of two immiscible substances is called a/an

    a. compound   c. suspension

    b. emulsion   d. element

78. The pH scale is used to specify the degree of acidity or

    a. salt content   c. alkalinity

    b. oxide content   d. metal content

79. Pure water, with a pH of 7, is considered to be

    a. neutral   c. acid

    b. salty   d. alkaline

80. Hard water can be made suitable for salon purposes by distillation or the use of

    a. acid   c. alum

    b. alcohol   d. water softener

81. The main ingredient in a water-in-oil emulsion is

    a. water   c. thickener

    b. oil   d. baking soda

82. The main ingredient in an oil-in-water emulsion is

    a. water   c. thickener

    b. oil   d. baking soda

83. A substance having the ability to attract water to itself is

    a. witch hazel   c. boric acid

    b. phenol   d. a humectant

84. Soaps having a pH above 9.5 are considered to be

    a. oxide   c. acid

    b. neutral   d. alkaline

85. A cream used for lubricating the skin during massage is

    a. hormone cream   c. vanishing cream

    b. emollient cream   d. suntan cream

86. An element widely used as an astringent is

    a. calamine lotion   c. witch hazel

    b. face powder   d. moisturizing cream

87. "Slip" and "bloom" are terms used to describe qualities found in

    a. lipstick   c. cleansing cream

    b. face powder   d. moisturizing cream

88. The federal agency responsible for enforcing rules and regulations regarding cosmetic products is called the

    a. Cosmetology State Board   c. Department of Licensing

    b. Food and Drug Administration   d. Department of Consumer Education

89. The federal agency responsible for regulating cosmetic advertising is the

    a. Federal Trade Commission   c. cosmetology state board

    b. Food and Drug Administration   d. Department of Consumer Education

90. The three forms of matter are solids, liquids, and

    a. water   c. gases

    b. earth   d. metal

91. Organic substances are not soluble in

    a. alcohol   c. petroleum

    b. benzene   d. water

92. The tendency of the atoms of an element to combine with other elements is called its

    a. physical activity

    c. chemical activity

    b. specific gravity

    d. chemical property

93. The alteration of the properties of matter without the formation of any new substance is called a/an

    a. physical change

    c. chemical mixture

    b. chemical change

    d. oxide mixture

94. The alteration of the properties of matter in such a way that a new substance is formed is called a/an

    a. chemical mixture

    c. chemical change

    b. physical change

    d. acid compound

95. The gaseous mixture that makes up the earth's atmosphere is

    a. air

    c. oxygen

    b. helium

    d. nitrogen

96. The pH of the skin mantle is

    a. 4.5

    c. 5.5

    b. 7.5

    d. 6.5

97. A powerful antiseptic and disinfectant that is obtained by the fermentation of certain sugars is

    a. ammonia

    c. alum

    b. alcohol

    d. sodium

98. A preparation used for the temporary removal of superfluous hair is a/an

    a. caustic

    c. carbolic acid

    b. astringent

    d. depilatory

99. The Federal Food and Drug Administration has jurisdiction over

    a. consumer complaints

    c. drug advertising

    b. salon services

    d. cosmetology licensing

100. Cosmetics can be kept fresh longer by being kept in a

    a. dark spot

    c. refrigerator

    b. warm cabinet

    d. dry sterilizer

Multiple Choice or Selection Test

Carefully read each statement. Underline the word or phrase which correctly completes the meaning of the statement.

1. The process by which food is assimilated and converted into tissue in living organisms is called

   a. sanitation   c. nutrition

   b. sterilization   d. mastication

2. The process utilized by the living body in building up and breaking down tissues is known as

   a. nutrition   c. sanitation

   b. metabolism   d. sterilization

3. The three basic food groups are fats, carbohydrates, and

   a. calories   c. minerals

   b. vitamins   d. proteins

4. Proteins are composed of various combinations of

   a. starches   c. amino acids

   b. vitamins   d. carbohydrates

5. Essential amino acids are those that

   a. the body manufactures   c. people are born with

   b. are acquired from food   d. are developed in infancy

6. The lengthwise chains of amino acids are called

   a. cystine chains   c. sulphur chains

   b. end bonds   d. polypeptide chains

7. An example of a food high in protein is

   a. soda   c. white bread

   b. candy   d. beans

8. The term used to describe and measure the available energy from various foods is

   a. calorie   c. chain

   b. end bond   d. ounce

9. Foods containing whole grains belong to the group known as

   a. dairy

   b. bread-cereal

   c. vegetable-fruit

   d. meat and protein

10. Essential ingredients to life, without which the body cannot survive for more than a few days, are

    a. carbohydrates

    b. vitamins

    c. proteins

    d. liquids

11. Scurvy, which produces ugly skin lesions, shows a deficiency in

    a. iron

    b. vitamin A

    c. vitamin C

    d. water

12. Skin that has a yellowish cast is indicative of a disease called

    a. scurvy

    b. jaundice

    c. pellagra

    d. psoriasis

13. An individual's sensitivity to a particular substance is called

    a. disease

    b. malnutrition

    c. an allergy

    d. a deficiency

14. The most important carbohydrate is

    a. protein

    b. fat

    c. glucose

    d. sulfur

15. Disturbed thoughts, extreme anxiety, delusions, and other symptoms of mental illness may be the result of a

    a. balanced diet

    b. polypeptide

    c. nutritional therapy

    d. chemical imbalance

16. Skin having a yellowish cast may be an indication of a/an

    a. attack of pellagra

    b. psoriasis infection

    c. dermatitis depression

    d. liver ailment

17. It is desirable for the salon to have a special consultation area because

    a. the light is better

    b. more space is available

    c. it helps sell products

    d. it ensures privacy

18. Many male patrons have minor skin irritation caused by

    a. shaving practices

    b. acne vulgaris

    c. psoriasis

    d. seborrhea

19. When discussing the cost of skin care treatments, the esthetician should

    a. price each treatment separately

    b. offer a series of treatments

    c. avoid talking about it

    d. price treatments according to each client's means

20. The esthetician should begin the client's record card

    a. during the consultation visit

    b. as soon as the client becomes a regular customer

    c. as soon as treatment is begun

    d. after the first treatment

21. If the esthetician detects a skin disease during the consultation, he or she should

    a. proceed with normal treatments

    b. recommend more frequent treatments

    c. refer the client to a dermatologist

    d. try to correct the condition

22. Skin that has sufficient moisture and sebum is classified as

    a. aging skin

    b. dry skin

    c. normal skin

    d. couperose skin

23. Loose, crepey, wrinkled skin is an indication of

    a. aging skin

    b. dry skin

    c. normal skin

    d. couperose skin

24. Small broken capillaries on the skin are a sign of

    a. a lack of moisture

    b. dry skin

    c. oily skin

    d. couperose skin

25. An overabundance of sebum produces

    a. couperose skin

    b. oily skin

    c. dry skin

    d. normal skin

26. Stimulating the sebaceous glands to produce sebum will help to correct

    a. acne skin

    b. normal skin

    c. dry skin

    d. couperose skin

27. A coating of crusts of greasy scales on the skin often is a sign of

   a. milia   c. comedones

   b. seborrhea   d. cystic acne

28. The continuous consumption of excessive alcohol and heavily spiced foods may lead to a condition known as

   a. acne simplex   c. rosacea

   b. seborrhea   d. dry skin

29. The skin is restored to a normal pH and the pores temporarily tightened by the use of

   a. an astringent   c. cleansing cream

   b. water   d. soap

30. Aftershave lotions act in the same way as

   a. a caustic   c. bacteria

   b. a disinfectant   d. an astringent

31. When skin is dry and irritated after shaving, it is advisable to apply

   a. bactericide lotion   c. moisturizing lotion

   b. high fragrance lotion   d. disinfectant lotion

32. Treatment for acne is designed to normalize the production of

   a. perspiration   c. follicles

   b. sebum   d. papillae

33. Dry skin is lacking in

   a. capillaries   c. sebum

   b. cortex   d. blood

34. Skin that lacks moisture is said to be

   a. matured   c. anemic

   b. dehydrated   d. senile

35. A type of skin that has both dry and oily areas is called

   a. discolored skin   c. couperose skin

   b. senile skin   d. combination skin

36. The natural aging processes of the body often result in

    a. dry skin
    b. excess sebum
    c. oily skin
    d. seborrhea

37. Aging skin often is lacking in

    a. elasticity
    b. tension
    c. texture
    d. follicles

38. Excessive washing of the skin with harsh products may result in the removal of the skin's

    a. texture balance
    b. acid mantle
    c. alkaline cover
    d. follicles

39. Accumulations of darkened sebum underneath the surface of the skin are called

    a. seborrhea
    b. blackheads
    c. whiteheads
    d. pits

40. Broken capillaries that can be seen beneath the surface of the skin are characteristic of

    a. acne skin
    b. couperose skin
    c. seborrhea skin
    d. rosacea skin

41. Cotton pads and compresses should be prepared

    a. when the client arrives
    b. before the treatment begins
    c. several days prior to their use
    d. during the treatment to ensure freshness

42. Eye pads should be large enough to cover the

    a. eyes and forehead
    b. eyes and nose
    c. entire eye area
    d. eyes, forehead, and nose

43. The cotton compress mask is usually about 4" wide and

    a. 2" long
    b. 6" long
    c. 4" long
    d. 9" long

44. The application of the cleansing product should begin on the client's

    a. forehead
    b. cheeks
    c. chin
    d. neck

45. Removal of cleanser from the female client's face always is begun at the base of the neck, using

    a. upward strokes
    b. downward strokes
    c. circular movements
    d. massage manipulations

46. Sponges used during the cleansing procedure are kept

    a. on a clean towel
    b. in lukewarm water
    c. in a wet sanitizer
    d. in a dry cabinet

47. The cotton compress mask is used to

    a. massage the client's skin
    b. remove the treatment mask
    c. protect the client's face
    d. keep the facial mask intact

48. The cotton compress mask consists of

    a. one piece of cotton
    b. five pieces of cotton
    c. two pieces of cotton
    d. three pieces of cotton

49. Pads and compresses should be stored in a

    a. dispersing cabinet
    b. covered container
    c. wet sanitizer
    d. storage cabinet

50. Cleansing with sponges is started on the neck with a/an

    a. up and down movement
    b. upward movement
    c. side to side movement
    d. downward movement

51. Massage promotes warmth as the blood supply and circulation are

    a. reduced
    b. temporarily stopped
    c. maintained
    d. increased

52. Massage movements are not performed on skin that

    a. is aged
    b. is already healthy
    c. is overly dry
    d. has abrasions

53. The massage movement in which the skin is grasped between the thumb and forefinger is called

    a. petrissage
    b. effleurage
    c. rolling
    d. tapping

54. Effleurage, a continuous, low movement applied with the fingers and palms, is also known as

    a. stroking

    b. kneading

    c. circular friction

    d. wringing

55. The kneading movement is also known as

    a. rolling

    b. stroking

    c. effleurage

    d. petrissage

56. Fulling, a movement used mainly on the client's arms, is a form of

    a. stroking

    b. shaking

    c. petrissage

    d. tapping

57. Tapping, slapping, and hacking movements are known as "tapotement" and

    a. percussion movements

    b. wringing movements

    c. circular friction

    d. rolling movements

58. Tapping movements must be light and digital to be suitable for

    a. arm massage

    b. facial massage

    c. hand massage

    d. shoulder massage

59. Rapid muscle contractions in the esthetician's arms produce the massage movement known as shaking or

    a. chucking

    b. rolling

    c. vibrating

    d. kneading

60. If it becomes necessary for the esthetician to interrupt a massage treatment, the hands should

    a. come to a sudden stop on the client's face

    b. stop movement and be lifted quickly from the face

    c. remain on the client's face

    d. be feathered off the client's face

61. The standard massage is often finished with

    a. brow movements

    b. the infrared lamp

    c. eye movements

    d. cheekbone movements

62. When using the standard massage, the movements on the chest, back, and shoulders are usually done with

    a. tapping movements

    b. circular movements

    c. vibrating movements

    d. feathering movements

63. The main purpose of massage 1 is the continuation of the

    a. deep penetration   c. application of emollients

    b. cleansing procedure   d. use of the vaporizer

64. Massage 2 should be done

    a. together with the cleansing procedures   c. before the cleansing procedure

    b. after the cleansing procedures   d. during the cleansing procedure

65. Massage 2 is done with

    a. tapping movements   c. effleurage movements

    b. vibrating movements   d. petrissage movements

66. Massage 2 should be followed by a

    a. thorough cleansing with cream   c. treatment mask

    b. kneading treatment   d. machine treatment

67. The massage best suited for acne skin is called

    a. massage 1   c. standard massage

    b. massage 2   d. Dr. Jacquet massage

68. The purpose of Dr. Jacquet massage is to

    a. help empty the oil ducts   c. prevent the movement of sebum

    b. prepare for disincrustation   d. cleanse acne skin

69. Kneading movements are not done in the area of the

    a. eyes   c. cheekbones

    b. chin   d. neck

70. When giving a facial massage it is important to follow a procedure that is

    a. unorthodox   c. easy

    b. systematic   d. disconnected

71. Effleurage is applied for its

    a. relaxing effects   c. invigorating effects

    b. stimulating effects   d. heating effects

72. Friction massage stimulates circulation and

    a. muscle relaxation

    c. stroking movements

    b. glandular activity

    d. heating effects

73. A massage movement that is performed by grasping the flesh firmly in one hand and moving the hand up and down along the bone is

    a. chucking

    c. fulling

    b. rolling

    d. kneading

74. At the beginning of a massage treatment, a few manipulations on right motor points will induce

    a. relaxation

    c. discoloration

    b. tension

    d. immobility

75. A massage method that is especially effective in treating oily skin is the

    a. effleurage method

    c. Dr. Jacquet method

    b. chucking method

    d. rolling method

76. An ingredient used in masks that has a mild antiseptic and astringent quality is

    a. sulfur

    c. zinc oxide

    b. magnesium

    d. glycerine

77. A mask ingredient that is capable of dissolving dead surface cells on the skin is

    a. sulfur

    c. glycerine

    b. calamine

    d. almond oil

78. The two most common forms of professional masks are clay and

    a. powder

    c. liquid

    b. dry

    d. gel

79. Mask application usually begins on the client's

    a. forehead

    c. chin

    b. cheeks

    d. neck

80. Custom-designed masks, containing natural ingredients, are usually formulated because they

    a. meet special problems

    c. are more beneficial to the skin

    b. have no allergic reaction

    d. are easier to prepare

81. Gauze is used primarily to

   a. keep the mask sterile   c. hold the facial mask together

   b. allow the skin to breathe   d. permit the client to see better

82. The facial mask that is popular for its instant and impressive results is the

   a. clay mask   c. herbal jelly mask

   b. wax mask   d. yeast mask

83. The wax mask should be allowed to build up until it is at least

   a. 1/4" thick   c. 1" thick

   b. 1/2" thick   d. 3/4" thick

84. When the wax mask is ready to be taken off, the first area to be removed is the

   a. bridge of the nose   c. neck

   b. left cheekbone   d. forehead

85. Clay, used in clay masks, produces a healing action that is beneficial in

   a. increasing temperature   c. refreshing the skin

   b. reducing inflammation   d. deepening color

86. The wax mask is not recommended for

   a. acne skin   c. dry skin

   b. aging skin   d. dehydrated skin

87. After the wax mask is removed, the face is cleaned with a mild

   a. astringent   c. paraffin

   b. disinfectant   d. uric acid

88. The important results that are achieved by the use of masks are toning, hydrating, and

   a. stimulating   c. tightening

   b. calming   d. toughening

89. Facial masks with ingredients that do not cling or hold to the face require a base layer of

   a. gauze   c. paste

   b. yeast   d. calamine

90. An ingredient used in masks for its toning, tightening, and hydrating effect is

   a. oatmeal   c. honey

   b. yogurt   d. yeast

TEST VI

Multiple Choice or Selection Test

Carefully read each statement. Underline the word or phrase which correctly completes the meaning of the statement.

1. It is important to be able to give facial treatments without machines because

   a. it is easier to perform such treatments   c. machines are complicated and difficult to use

   b. machines may not be available   d. better results are achieved without machines

2. Towels that are best suited for steaming the face are made of

   a. gauze   c. very thin rayon

   b. terrycloth   d. nylon

3. When giving a facial for normal skin, massage 1 usually follows

   a. astringent massage   c. towel steaming

   b. high-frequency treatment   d. infrared lamp treatment

4. When giving a facial for normal skin, the esthetician may leave the infrared lamp on during

   a. massage 2   c. the standard massage

   b. massage 1   d. the cleansing treatment

5. Terrycloth towels are best suited for steaming the face because they

   a. cool faster   c. hold heat longer

   b. stimulate the skin   d. dehydrate the skin

6. Alternative facial treatments that can be used for normal skin include the wax mask treatment and the

   a. dehydrated skin facial   c. oily skin facial

   b. epidermabrasion treatment   d. dry skin facial

7. When giving a facial for dry skin, the treatment cream may be left on during the mask treatment providing it is not of an oily texture and is

    a. based in oil

    b. water soluble

    c. insoluble in water

    d. a disinfectant

8. When giving a facial for acne skin, the following procedure is omitted:

    a. wax mask

    b. suction

    c. carbonic spray

    d. epidermabrasion

9. When giving a facial for a combination skin, apply cotton compresses saturated with disincrustation lotion to

    a. oily areas with blackheads

    b. overly dry skin areas

    c. normal skin areas

    d. the entire face and neck

10. The only massage the esthetician should perform on acne skin is

    a. massage 1

    b. massage 2

    c. the standard massage

    d. the Dr. Jacquet movement

11. During the special acne treatment

    a. use the Dr. Jacquet movement

    b. use only massage 1

    c. use only massage 2

    d. use only the standard massage

12. The procedure that softens and emulsifies grease deposits and blackheads in the follicles is known as

    a. the Dr. Jacquet Massage

    b. dermabrasion

    c. epidermabrasion

    d. disincrustation

13. The infrared lamp and ice must never be used on skin that

    a. has acne blemishes

    b. is oil dry

    c. has broken capillaries

    d. is considered a combination skin

14. The term "couperose" is used to describe skin that

    a. has broken capillaries

    b. has acne blemishes

    c. is excessively dry

    d. is excessively oily

15. The treatment dealing with cosmetic peeling on the outermost surface of the skin is known as

    a. deep cleansing

    b. epidermabrasion

    c. dermabrasion

    d. disincrustation

16. Skin that is flaky and has superficial lines, due to lack of water, is called

    a. oily skin

    b. normal skin

    c. astringent skin

    d. dehydrated skin

17. The treatment for dehydrated skin requires the addition of a/an

    a. disinfectant

    b. ice cube

    c. moisturizer

    d. salon solution

18. A facial cream that is too heavy can interfere with the natural production of

    a. growth cells

    b. blood cells

    c. capillaries

    d. sebum

19. Acne is a manifestation of body changes that take place especially during

    a. pregnancy

    b. childhood

    c. adolescence

    d. middle age

20. Acne pimples are ripe for extraction when they have a

    a. hard core center

    b. bluish tinge

    c. light pink center

    d. light yellowish head

21. The primary purpose of an epidermabrasion (skin peeling) treatment is to remove

    a. hair follicles

    b. dead surface cells

    c. acne pimples

    d. oily skin

22. A substance that can transmit an electrical current is known as a/an

    a. conductor

    b. pipe

    c. insulator

    d. nonconductor

23. A substance that resists the passage of an electrical current is known as a/an

    a. conductor

    b. insulator

    c. converter

    d. rectifier

24. An electrical current that flows constantly in one direction is called

    a. AC current

    b. faradic current

    c. alternating current

    d. direct current

25. An electrical current that flows first in one direction and then in the other is called

    a. direct current   c. DC current

    b. alternating current   d. amperage

26. A unit of electrical pressure is referred to as a/an

    a. ampere   c. ohm

    b. volt   d. watt

27. An ampere is a unit of electrical

    a. resistance   c. strength

    b. pressure   d. tension

28. An ohm is a unit of electrical

    a. pressure   c. tension

    b. strength   d. resistance

29. A milliamperemeter measures the rate of the flow of

    a. electric current   c. water

    b. heat rays   d. light rays

30. The Tesla current is the common name for a

    a. infrared ray   c. low-frequency current

    b. ultraviolet ray   d. current with a high rate of oscillation

31. An electrical current used for its heat-producing effects is the

    a. faradic current   c. high-frequency current

    b. low-frequency current   d. galvanic current

32. Polarity refers to poles in an electrical current that are

    a. similar   c. alike

    b. duplicates   d. opposites

33. The positive pole may be used to

    a. stimulate nerves   c. soften skin tissues

    b. increase blood supply   d. close the pores

34. The main function of the galvanic machine is to introduce into the skin

   a. insoluble products   c. a carbonic gas spray

   b. water-soluble products   d. moist vapors

35. The process whereby the galvanic machine introduces acid (pH) products into the skin is known as

   a. anaphoresis   c. cataphoresis

   b. conduction   d. phoresis

36. Use of the negative pole will result in

   a. an alkaline reaction   c. soothed nerves

   b. an acid reaction   d. decreased blood supply

37. During the disincrustation procedure, the positive pole on the galvanic machine should

   a. be held in the client's hand   c. not be held at all

   b. be held by the esthetician   d. not be connected to the machine

38. The appearance of a violet ray is characteristic when using the

   a. ionto rollers   c. galvanic machine

   b. positive and negative poles   d. high-frequency machine

39. Tesla current is the same as

   a. galvanic current   c. ultraviolet rays

   b. slow oscillation   d. high-frequency current

40. The use of high-frequency current will

   a. decrease blood circulation   c. decrease glandular activity

   b. increase blood circulation   d. generate cooling currents

41. The primary purpose of the brushing machine is to

   a. soothe the skin   c. slough off dead cells

   b. increase circulation   d. produce heat

42. The atomizer is the same as the

   a. high-frequency machine   c. crushing machine

   b. galvanic machine   d. spray machine

43. The skin care machine that acts as a vacuum is called the

    a. facial vaporizer

    b. carbonic gas spray

    c. suction machine

    d. electric pulverizer

44. The suction machine may be used for all skin types with the exception of

    a. excessively dry skin

    b. heavily couperosed skin

    c. very oily skin

    d. blemished skin

45. The carbonic gas spray is used primarily on

    a. oily skins

    b. flaky skins

    c. dry skins

    d. couperose skins

46. The Wood's lamp employs the use of

    a. heat rays

    b. violet rays

    c. infrared rays

    d. invisible rays

47. When using the Wood's lamp, pigmentation and dark spots on the skin will be visible as

    a. blue-white areas

    b. yellow and pink areas

    c. white spots

    d. brown areas

48. Ultraviolet rays are

    a. infrared

    b. heat-producing

    c. cold, invisible rays

    d. cold, visible rays

49. A constant and direct current rectified to a safe, low-voltage level is called the

    a. high-frequency current

    b. galvanic current

    c. low-frequency level

    d. Tesla current

50. A safety device that prevents the overheating of electrical wires is called a/an

    a. fuse

    b. ohm

    c. circuit

    d. nonconductor

51. An instrument that serves as a conductor and applicator of electricity to certain areas of the body is called a/an

    a. galvanizer

    b. rectifier

    c. electrode

    d. rheostat

52. Having opposite poles in electrical current is known as

    a. polarity

    c. anaphoresis

    b. phoresis

    d. galvanism

53. The process by which chemical solutions are forced into unbroken skin by means of a galvanic current is called

    a. anabolism

    c. phoresis

    b. polarity

    d. galvanism

54. The process that softens and liquefies grease deposits in the follicles is called

    a. ionization

    c. vaporization

    b. cataphoresis

    d. disincrustation

55. For the ionization to work properly, the cream or lotion applied must be

    a. alcohol-based

    c. water-soluble

    b. oil-soluble

    d. negative pole

56. When treating delicate or dry skin with the brushing machine, it is advisable to use a

    a. coarse brush

    c. hand brush

    b. medium hard brush

    d. soft brush

57. The spray machine also is known as a/an

    a. atomizer

    c. galvanizer

    b. disincrustator

    d. photostat

58. The suction machine is helpful in

    a. treating couperosed skin

    c. sloughing off dead cells

    b. deep pore cleansing

    d. treating broken capillaries

59. The spray machine serves to stimulate nerve endings and

    a. decrease circulation

    c. destroy pigmentation

    b. activate cell metabolism

    d. increase ionization

60. The electric mask is used to facilitate

    a. surface cleansing

    c. deep pore penetration

    b. acne treatments

    d. increased ionization

61. The action of ultraviolet rays is both chemical and

a. germicidal

c. diagnostic

b. cleansing

d. illuminating

62. Overexposure to ultraviolet rays may cause tissue

a. destruction

c. relaxation

b. growth

d. stimulation

63. The machine the esthetician will first use when giving a facial for any skin type is the

a. electric pulverizer

c. carbonic gas spray

b. high-frequency machine

d. vaporizer

64. If used, the brushing machine will follow

a. massage 1

c. massage 2

b. the vaporizer

d. the galvanic machine

65. When applied, the suction machine usually will precede

a. massage 1

c. the brushing machine

b. the vaporizer

d. massage 2

66. The esthetician will use the carbonic gas spray in treating skin that is oily and/or

a. combination

c. couperose

b. aging

d. acne

67. When treating couperose skin, it is important that the vaporizer be placed

a. farther away than for other skin types

c. approximately the same for all other skin types

b. closer than for other skin types

d. close enough to maintain a hot temperature

68. The facial spray is generally used immediately following the

a. removal of the facial mask

c. application of protective fluid

b. cleansing procedure

d. blotting of the face

69. When treating oily skin, the suction machine is used following the

a. removal of the treatment mask

c. disincrustation procedure

b. galvanic ionization

d. electric mask

70. Deep penetration of treatment cream may be accomplished with massage 2, high-frequency current, an electric machine, and

    a. a suction machine   c. galvanic ionization

    b. a spray machine   d. a facial vaporizer

71. Disincrustation is not done on

    a. normal skin   c. protein skin

    b. oily skin   d. dry skin

72. One of the methods to achieve deep penetrations is

    a. suction   c. galvanic ionization

    b. vaporization   d. pulverization

73. All massage movements on mature skin must be performed gently to avoid

    a. moisturizing the skin   c. lubricating the skin

    b. dehydrating the skin   d. stretching the skin

74. When the skin is extremely oily, it should be given a thorough

    a. lubrication treatment   c. disincrustation

    b. sebaceous stimulation   d. oil treatment

75. The beginning of treatments on skin with a long acne history may result in a sudden

    a. galvanic ionization   c. disincrustation

    b. improvement   d. flare-up

TEST VII

Multiple Choice or Selection Test

Carefully read each statement. Underline the word or phrase which correctly completes the meaning of the statement.

1. Temporary removal of unwanted hair can be accomplished by the use of

    a. depilatories   c. short wave

    b. diathermy   d. electrolysis

2. Permanent removal of unwanted hair is accomplished by

    a. tweezers   c. electrolysis

    b. depilatories   d. waxing

3. Chemical hair removers in the form of creams, pastes, or powders are called

    a. diathermy removers   c. electrolysis removers

    b. depilatories   d. short wave removers

4. A skin test is necessary before removing superfluous hair by the application of

    a. chemical depilatories   c. electrolysis

    b. short wave treatment   d. hot wax

5. Wax depilatories should never be applied over warts, moles, growths, or abrasions because they may cause

    a. an allergy   c. an irritation

    b. discoloration   d. a carbuncle

6. A wax depilatory should always be applied to the skin in the direction that is the

    a. opposite of hair growth   c. easiest to apply

    b. same as hair growth   d. most comfortable to the client

7. A wax depilatory should be removed from the skin in the direction that is the

    a. least painful to the client   c. same as the hair growth

    b. opposite to hair growth   d. easiest for the esthetician

8. Removal of superfluous hair by the waxing procedure should be followed by the application of

    a. a chemical depilatory   c. cleansing lotion

    b. medicated lotion   d. talcum powder

9. Excessive growth of hair is known as

    a. papilla   c. hypertrichosis

    b. thermolysis   d. trichoptilosis

10. The short-wave method of hair removal destroys the papilla by

    a. changes   c. coagulation

    b. current   d. decomposition

11. The short-wave method of electrolysis employs a

    a. double needle   c. multiple needle

    b. single needle   d. triple needle

12. The galvanic method of hair removal destroys the papilla by

    a. hypertrichosis   c. thermolysis

    b. coagulation   d. decomposition

13. The galvanic method of hair removal is also known as the

    a. double-needle method   c. single-needle method

    b. triple-needle method   d. multiple-needle method

14. Chemical depilatories usually are left on the skin for approximately

    a. 1-2 minutes   c. 30-40 minutes

    b. 5-10 minutes   d. 45-60 minutes

15. Where there are large areas of superfluous hair, such as on the arms and legs, the client may find it desirable to remove hair by

    a. galvanic   c. short wave

    b. tweezing   d. shaving

16. An electrologist should not treat clients suffering with

    a. hirsuties   c. diabetes

    b. acne   d. keratin

17. Removal of the hair by the root is called

    a. epilation   c. hypertrichosis

    b. diathermy   d. hirsuties

18. Electrologists should never remove hair from

    a. chin   c. moles

    b. cheeks   d. wrists

19. The hair is usually removed from the eyebrows by

    a. electrolysis   c. lightening

    b. tweezing   d. chemicals

20. Following a wax hair removal treatment, the skin should be bathed with a/an

a. cresol lotion

c. disinfectant lotion

b. medicated lotion

d. formalin lotion

21. Strong sunlight will cause freckles to

a. become less prominent

c. multiply

b. darken in color

d. peel off the skin

22. To protect the skin against the sun's harmful effects, advise clients to use

a. baby oil

c. suntan oil

b. suntan lotion

d. sunscreen lotion

23. Drugs and alcohol when used by clients in large quantities will adversely affect the skin because they tend to interfere with the body's intake of

a. liquids

c. oxygen

b. air

d. water

24. The study of the face and features as related to the character of an individual is known as

a. physiognomy

c. physiology

b. psychology

d. anatomy

25. The term "standard facelift" refers to a standard plastic (cosmetic) surgery procedure known as

a. rhinoplasty

c. blepharoplasty

b. lipectomy

d. rhytidectomy

26. Wrinkles around the eyes are corrected by the surgical procedure known as

a. blepharoplasty

c. lipectomy

b. rhytidectomy

d. rhinoplasty

27. Plastic surgery of the nose is called

a. rhinoplasty

c. blepharoplasty

b. rhytidectomy

d. lipectomy

28. The application of a caustic substance to the skin is a surgical procedure known as chemical skin refining or

a. tattooing

c. dermabrasion

b. peeling

d. epidermabrasion

29. Premature wrinkling and sagging of the skin can be caused by rapid

   a. exercising   c. running

   b. weight gain   d. weight loss

30. The human skin ages due to the deterioration of the

   a. cuticle level   c. red corpuscles

   b. elastic tissue   d. white corpuscle

31. Beauty care in which aromatic oils are used as active ingredients is called

   a. psychotherapy   c. formaltherapy

   b. hydrotherapy   d. aromatherapy

32. Aromatherapy is primarily used in salons to induce

   a. relaxation   c. stimulation

   b. invigoration   d. excitement

33. Clove, thyme, sandalwood, and lavender have actions that are

   a. antiseptic   c. aging

   b. stimulating   d. relaxing

34. A fragrance that is a medley of fragrances is called

   a. a bouquet   c. spice

   b. fruit   d. one-flower

35. Cinnamon, cloves, vanilla, and ginger are used to create a fragrance called

   a. woodsy blend   c. fruity blend

   b. spicy blend   d. floral blend

36. Sandalwood, rosewood, and cedar are some of the herbs and plants used to make

   a. floral blends   c. fruity blends

   b. spicy blends   d. forest blends

37. One of the important methods used to obtain oils and essences used in fragrances is by

   a. distillation   c. grinding

   b. rolling   d. crushing

38. Distillation of aromatic essences is achieved by the use of

   a. iced water   c. heated oil

   b. boiling water   d. freezing

39. A method used to press essential oils out of substances is

   a. extraction   c. expression

   b. distillation   d. effleurage

40. Plunging flower petals into hot fat in order to absorb their essential oils is called

   a. extraction   c. effleurage

   b. maceration   d. expression

41. Fixatives for the manufacture of fragrances are obtained from

   a. flower oils   c. cinnamon oils

   b. animal oils   d. sandalwood

42. The green coloring matter found in plants is

   a. salicylic acid   c. chlorophyll

   b. caraway   d. cascarilla

43. An antiseptic frequently used in acne treatment is

   a. cinnamon extract   c. salicylic acid

   b. chlorophyll juice   d. cascarilla oil

44. A substance that has a calming and soothing effect on the skin is

   a. camomile   c. thyme

   b. eucalyptus   d. fennel

45. An agent used for its healing qualities is

   a. magnolia   c. rosemary

   b. comfrey   d. rhubarb

46. It is impossible to become a successful makeup artist without an understanding of the basic principles of the use of

   a. heights   c. distance

   b. distribution   d. color

47. The pigment that gives skin its color is

    a. hemoglobin

    b. melanin

    c. carotene

    d. keratin

48. The pigment that gives red blood cells their color is

    a. hemoglobin

    b. melanin

    c. carotene

    d. keratin

49. A person who has melanocyte cells that do not produce melanin is

    a. carotene

    b. an albino

    c. tertiary

    d. triadic

50. Red, yellow, and blue are called

    a. secondary colors

    b. tertiary colors

    c. primary colors

    d. intense colors

51. Colors created by mixing equal amounts of two of the primary colors are called

    a. tertiary colors

    b. intense colors

    c. carotene colors

    d. secondary colors

52. Colors achieved by mixing a secondary color with a primary color are called

    a. carotene colors

    b. tertiary colors

    c. triadic colors

    d. intense colors

53. A color as the eye perceives it is called its

    a. hue

    b. shade

    c. value

    d. intensity

54. The lightness or darkness of a color is its

    a. hue

    b. intensity

    c. value

    d. tint

55. The brightness or dullness of a color is its

    a. value

    b. shade

    c. hue

    d. intensity

56. The low color value or the darkness of the color is its

    a. intensity   c. shade

    b. tint   d. hue

57. The high color value or lightness of the color is its

    a. intensity   c. value

    b. hue   d. tint

58. The use of one color in a costume is a color scheme that is

    a. complementary   c. triadic

    b. monochromatic   d. analogous

59. The use of three adjacent colors is referred to as a color scheme that is

    a. monochromatic   c. analogous

    b. triadic   d. complementary

60. A combination achieved by using three colors that are an equal distance apart on the color wheel is a color scheme called

    a. triadic   c. monochromatic

    b. analogous   d. complementary

61. The combining of two hues that are directly opposite on the color wheel is a color scheme that is

    a. analogous   c. tertiary

    b. complementary   d. primary

62. Bright colors make the area covered appear

    a. narrower   c. receding

    b. smaller   d. larger

63. Dull and dark colors make the area covered appear

    a. smaller   c. longer

    b. larger   d. taller

64. Blue, green, and purple are referred to as

    a. warm colors   c. cool colors

    b. hot colors   d. neutral colors

65. Pink, brown, and red are referred to as

   a. warm colors

   b. cool colors

   c. neutral colors

   d. mixed colors

66. Black and white are called

   a. primary colors

   b. neutral colors

   c. cool colors

   d. triad colors

67. Face powder may be colorless or matched to the color of the

   a. lip rouge

   b. eye color

   c. cheek color

   d. foundation

68. The main objective when applying makeup is to improve the client's

   a. ego

   b. changes

   c. appearance

   d. status

69. Before applying the makeup, the client's face should be

   a. massaged

   b. cleansed

   c. powdered

   d. vaporized

70. The type of face that is used to form the basis for corrective makeup is the

   a. heart-shaped face

   b. round face

   c. oblong face

   d. oval face

71. On the ideal oval face, the space between the eyes is the width of the

   a. lips

   b. nose

   c. eye

   d. thumb

72. In the diamond-shaped face, the greatest facial width is across the

   a. jawline

   b. forehead

   c. eyeline

   d. cheekbones

73. The facial type in which the jawline is wider than the forehead is the

   a. pear-shaped face

   b. diamond-shaped face

   c. square face

   d. oblong face

74. The facial type that has greater length in proportion to its width is the

   a. square face

   b. round face

   c. heart-shaped face

   d. oblong face

75. When compared to the oval face, the facial shape that is broader in proportion to its length is the

   a. pear-shaped face

   b. diamond-shaped face

   c. round face

   d. oblong face

76. The square face is characterized by its straight lines, wide forehead, and square

   a. cheekbones

   b. jawline

   c. chinline

   d. eyeline

77. The narrow, pointed chin is characteristic of the

   a. oblong face

   b. heart-shaped face

   c. pear-shaped face

   d. oval-shaped face

78. Eyebrows should be properly tweezed in the direction

   a. opposite to natural growth

   b. of their natural growth

   c. toward the chin

   d. toward the scalp

79. Wide-set eyes will seem closer if the eyebrows are tweezed to a distance equal to the width of

   a. the nose

   b. the lips

   c. one eye

   d. the chin

80. To minimize close-set eyes, space the brows so that the distance between them equals the width of

   a. the nose

   b. the lips

   c. one eye

   d. the chin

81. The color and type of foundation used should be appropriate to the color and texture of the client's

   a. eyes

   b. hair

   c. eyebrows

   d. skin

82. The main purpose of the use of face powder is to

   a. hide blemishes

   b. cover creases

   c. set the foundation

   d. eliminate the use of foundation

83. Cheekcolor should not be applied closer to the nose than the center of the

   a. chin

   b. eye

   c. forehead

   d. lips

84. Eyeliner is applied to the edges of the

   a. eyelids

   b. eyebrows

   c. eye pupils

   d. lashes

85. For evening wear, eyeliner is applied to make the eyes appear more

   a. glamorous

   b. almond shaped

   c. subdued

   d. smaller

86. The application of a lighter cosmetic to a facial feature serves to

   a. detract from it

   b. retard it

   c. emphasize it

   d. minimize it

87. The application of darker cosmetics to facial features serves to

   a. exaggerate them

   b. minimize them

   c. emphasize them

   d. make them prominent

88. The use of lighter and darker makeup to minimize or cover defects and to emphasize good features is called

   a. grooming

   b. contouring

   c. designing

   d. structuring

89. The proper application of makeup helps to conceal

   a. wrinkles

   b. highlights

   c. blemishes

   d. lightening

90. When a makeup artist wants to make thin or small facial areas appear larger or fuller, those areas are treated with a

   a. darker foundation

   b. deeper foundation

   c. color foundation

   d. lighter foundation

91. Areas of the face that have wide or prominent features which must be minimized are covered with

   a. lighter foundation

   b. darker foundation

   c. deeper foundation

   d. color foundation

92. The eyes may be made to look larger and more expressive with the proper application of

    a. eyebrow color

    b. cheekcolor

    c. artificial eyelashes

    d. eye cream

93. To give the eyes a more flattering look, artificial lashes should be

    a. colored

    b. feathered

    c. shampooed

    d. lined

94. If artificial lashes are applied after the application of eyeliner they are harder to

    a. detect

    b. color

    c. feather

    d. clean

95. It is advisable to give an allergy test before applying

    a. eyeliner

    b. mascara

    c. individual eyelashes

    d. eyeshadow

96. Angling the individual lashes slightly inward serves to

    a. lengthen the lashes

    b. fill in sparse lashes

    c. make adhesive hold better

    d. thin out the lashes

97. Eyeshadow is usually applied only to the

    a. eyelashes

    b. upper eyelids

    c. lower eyelids

    d. eyebrows

98. Highlighting is usually done

    a. in the crease of the eye

    b. over the eyebrow

    c. underneath the eyebrow

    d. on the eyelid

99. To accentuate the eyes and make the eyelashes appear thicker, apply

    a. mascara

    b. foundation

    c. eyeshadow

    d. face cream

100. To make the eyelashes look thicker, longer, and darker, use

    a. eyeliner

    b. blusher

    c. mascara

    d. eyeshadow

Multiple Choice or Selection Test

Carefully read each statement. Underline the word or phrase which correctly completes the meaning of the statement.

1. A good location for a skin care salon is near a

   a. machine shop

   b. bowling alley

   c. tavern

   d. department store

2. State laws usually cover sales tax, licensure, and

   a. Social Security

   b. import duties

   c. Worker's Compensation

   d. excise taxes

3. Insurance policies are purchased by salon owners to protect themselves against suits for

   a. malpractice

   b. licensure

   c. malingering

   d. trespassing

4. The tone for the entire salon usually is set by the

   a. reception area

   b. parking facilities

   c. powder room

   d. dispensary

5. In a well organized salon, it is important to have

   a. outlandish colors

   b. a kitchen

   c. a classroom

   d. a dispensary

6. The best form of advertising is

   a. a pleased client

   b. direct mail

   c. a newspaper ad

   d. a window display

7. To be effective, advertising must create

   a. antagonism

   b. indifference

   c. desire

   d. neglect

8. A form of advertising that acts as a salesman to every person passing the salon is

   a. sky writing

   b. a radio broadcast

   c. an attractive window display

   d. a billboard

9. Salon failures often are the result of management

   a. cooperation   c. training

   b. inexperience   d. efficiency

10. Careless appointment booking methods often contribute to salon

    a. success   c. growth

    b. development   d. failure

11. Smooth salon operation depends on

    a. efficient management   c. business neglect

    b. insufficient capital   d. careless bookkeeping

12. The largest expense item in operating a salon is

    a. salaries   c. rent

    b. taxes   d. suppliers

13. All government tax laws make it mandatory that each business maintain proper

    a. employee lounges   c. business records

    b. sales displays   d. customer lists

14. Accurate daily records permit the evaluation of

    a. business progress   c. appointments

    b. customer relations   d. employee relations

15. An accurate and efficient control of supplies can be maintained only by having an organized

    a. inventory system   c. sales force

    b. purchasing order   d. depreciation record

16. Daily sales slips and petty cash books should be retained for at least

    a. 5 years   c. 3 years

    b. 6 months   d. 7 years

17. Salon owners should protect themselves against possible casualty losses by obtaining proper

    a. fire extinguishers   c. insurance

    b. sanitation   d. life preservers

18. An important part of a salon's business is handled by

    a. mail

    b. telephone

    c. messenger

    d. business meetings

19. Good telephone habits and techniques help to build up the salon's

    a. reputation

    b. appearance

    c. location

    d. gossip

20. Assigning a well trained person to handle telephone calls is evidence of

    a. wasted talent

    b. poor management

    c. good planning

    d. business inexperience

21. A clear speaking voice, correct speech, and a pleasant tone are all requisites of a good telephone

    a. posture

    b. personality

    c. instrument

    d. transformation

22. The properly used telephone is an important and valuable aid in

    a. increasing business

    b. reducing service

    c. avoiding creditors

    d. disparaging creditors

23. To protect the client, if a serious accident occurs, call

    a. the client's home

    b. an ambulance

    c. the manager

    d. a lawyer

24. The first step in successful selling in the salon is to

    a. be aggressive

    b. break down resistance

    c. discourage competition

    d. sell yourself

25. The foundation of good salesmanship is

    a. self-confidence

    b. impatience

    c. aggressiveness

    d. familiarity

26. The ability to do what is necessary without being told what and how to do it is referred to as

    a. initiative

    b. acquisitiveness

    c. assertiveness

    d. tact

27. Saying or doing the right thing at the right time, in the right place, and without any offense is known as

a. acquisitiveness

c. assertiveness

b. tact

d. impatience

28. The first consideration of the salesperson should be the client's

a. breakdown of resistance

c. financial condition

b. best interests

d. acquisitiveness

29. To create and maintain a good relationship with a client, always address him or her by

a. nickname

c. haircolor

b. familiar title

d. last name

30. For sales techniques to be successful, the language used should be

a. neutral

c. positive

b. negative

d. placid